COMBAT AND SURVIVAL

WHAT IT TAKES TO FIGHT AND WIN

VOLUME
23

Originally published in the United Kingdom in weekly parts **COMBAT & SURVIVAL**
is a study of the armed forces at work. It shows the skills taught to soldiers
and the way in which military units operate. It examines the weapons
and equipment used by different armies; and, by looking at recruit
training and exercises, **COMBAT & SURVIVAL** demonstrates
how the armed forces develop individual responsibility,
leadership and initiative.

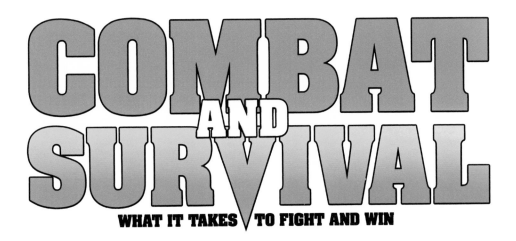

WHAT IT TAKES TO FIGHT AND WIN

VOLUME
23

H. S. STUTTMAN, INC. *publishers*   Westport, Connecticut 06889

Contents
Volume 23

Published by H. S. STUTTMAN INC.
Westport, Connecticut 06889
© Aerospace Publishing 1991
ISBN 0-87475-560-3

ASSAULT RIVER CROSSING

FLOTATION AIDS

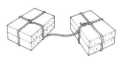

Jerry cans tied together make water wings. The rope goes across your chest and under your arms, leaving both arms free. Alternatively, hold a single can underneath your chest and kick with your legs.

Water bottles can be used in the same way as jerry cans. In the jungle, you will have issue water bags that look like the insides of wine boxes, and these are excellent for flotation.

Bergen liners, ponchos or fertiliser sacks can be used as flotation bags. You and all your kit can travel across in this way – as long as you are not carrying too much ammo – or you can send your kit over and retrieve the bag.

Polystyrene and other floating rubbish can be bundled up to make floats for you and your kit. Or you can pack it in your Bergen to make sure it stays above water.

The crossing of a major obstacle such as a river is normally planned at battalion level, but at platoon or section level you must be familiar with the various methods of crossing. A river obstacle will not always stop infantry on foot, but it will cause delay and expose you to enemy fire.

As a dismounted infantryman crossing a river at platoon level, you will be part of a larger plan and you should understand its outline. The battlegroup commander will normally divide his force into a **bank group**, an **assault group** and an **engineer group**.

On the modern battlefield, a crossing is much better mounted at night. Start the crossing silently, and have a pre-planned fire support programme on call in case the crossing is compromised: the engineer group is particularly vulnerable.

The bank group often consists of medium recce troops, with Scorpion and Scimitar recce vehicles, whose

Below: Extensive preparation of the banks is usually required for major bridging operations. Efficient recce can save you a great deal of time and effort. This monster, in service with the German army, is based on the Leopard chassis.

River crossing the hard way. It is certainly worth stripping off if the tactical situation allows, as drying kit in the field is always a problem. Always use a safety line: these crossings are usually done at night, and if you are clipped into the line you are less likely to get lost

Air defence
The Soviet air army has a fairly limited night ground-attack capability, but even so, air defence assets should be deployed to protect crossing sites, staging areas and the bridgehead. They must be in position and operational by first light.

Air superiority
You must have air superiority for any sizeable river crossing operation, as engineer assets are very vulnerable to air attack. But although a favourable air situation can be maintained for limited periods over sections of the battlefield, this is difficult to guarantee, so crossings will normally be attempted at night.

Heliborne assault
This is the faster way to establish the bridgehead but, like paradropping, it does have its disadvantages, especially if the crossing troops do not reach them in time!

Tactical air support
Large crossings will require air support from attack helicopters as well as ground attack aircraft.

Fire support
Massive fire support will be required to suppress the enemy on bridgehead objectives and the exit bank. Smoke can be used to mask the whole operation, and hopefully efficient counter-battery fire will reduce the damage inflicted by enemy indirect fire weapons – of which there is no shortage in Group Soviet Forces Germany.

Crossing site characteristics
Look for positions that have minimum exposure to enemy direct fire weapons; covered and concealed access to the river's edge; and gently sloping firm banks, free of obstacles, that permit rapid entry at multiple points.

Immediate objectives
Having crossed the river, you must secure the exit bank, protect the rest of the unit that is still crossing, and orientate the assaulting units to their intermediate or bridgehead objectives.

The bridgehead
This should be secured as soon as possible and enough ground left behind it for a fighting force to deploy.

GETTING ACROSS

There is no substitute for first-hand viewing of potential crossing sites. You as an infantryman will escort Royal Engineer recce of the river and banks, perhaps with engineer divers to survey the river bed. Recce patrols will also be needed to find out what the enemy is up to. Be careful: if you compromise the patrol, you also compromise the area of the crossing site. So use deception patrols in areas you are not interested in. The river crossing phases are:
1. Move to the river.
2. Assault crossing.
3. Advance from the exit bank.
4. Secure the bridgehead.

communications facilities enable them to provide the command and control facilities necessary to mount such a complex operation.

The **bank group** secures the home bank and assists the assaulting troops in mounting the operation, and is responsible for selecting and marking assembly areas and routes, establishing crossing sites, providing guides and traffic control posts, and evacuating the wounded.

Assault group

The **assault group** will normally consist of infantry, with as many ATGW systems as possible so that they can withstand tank attack; artillery Forward Observation Officers (FOOs); and Mortar Fire Controllers (MFCs). These are reinforced by armour as soon as a crossing site is opened.

You must establish the initial bridgehead as quickly as possible and expand it so that you can assemble a force which is big enough to break out. Any unnecessary delay will give the enemy time to recover from his initial surprise and counter-attack.

The more surprise you achieve, the greater your chance of success. Always attempt to deceive the enemy about your exact intentions to draw his reserves to the wrong place or at least delay and confuse his reaction.

Once you have established a foothold, the **engineer group** can begin to develop its bridge or ferry.

How do you, the infantryman, fit into the picture? Normally you will make your crossing in a recce boat or assault boat. But it may be, particularly in jungle or IS operations, that boats are not available and a river crossing has to be made nevertheless. Poor swimmers should aim to cross at the wider and consequently shallower and slower-flowing parts of the river. High banks on the far shore can indicate deep water, which could make it difficult for you and your men to leave the water. If you see sandbanks or shallow water in the centre of the stream, make the most of these as they provide an opportunity for reorgan-

Deception plan
Fake crossing points and assembly areas should be used to disguise the true battle picture from the enemy, and hopefully to attract some enemy indirect fire from the real crossing point.

Staging area
Units waiting to cross must have cover and concealment and a large enough area for vehicle and equipment dispersion.

Bridge defence
Once the bridge is up, defending it is the next problem. Among the options are the use of ground troops, heliborne assault, air attack, and tactical nuclear strike.

Assault troops
They must carry sufficient anti-tank weapons to fight off an enemy armoured counter attack. Forward observation officers (FOOs) and mortar fire controllers (MFCs) should be well forward with the assault troops to direct fire accurately onto the enemy.

Methods of river crossing
There are five basic methods: swimming, fording, bridging, rafting, and the use of assault boats.

When the combat engineer tractor has done the job on the banks of the river, the construction of the medium girder bridge using a portable pier leg goes into full swing.

AIM-OFF TECHNIQUE

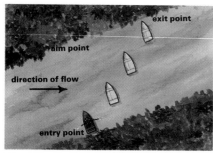

When crossing with amphibious vehicles or boats, you must compensate for the effect of river current. Pick an entry point upstream from where you want to exit and then aim the boat straight across the river. The side slip takes you to the exit point – with some luck and a little experience.

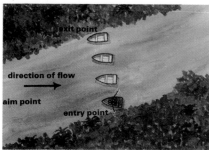

To exit a point directly across from the entry point, point the boat upstream as you paddle across to compensate for the river's speed. This technique does require practice to get it right for the varied rates of flow as you cross the river.

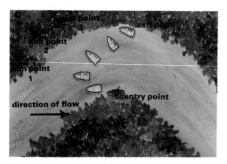

Alternatively, you can take advantage of the slack water on the inside of a bend in the river to combine both techniques, paddling upstream in the slack and compensating for the drift, and keeping your nose upstream.

isation and rest, and they allow you to regain your feet if you are in danger of being swept away.

Swim with the current

If you or one of your men get into real difficulties, swim with the current, easing yourself towards a bank and out of the water at the first opportunity. Do not try to swim against the current: this will quickly exhaust you and probably result in your drowning.

When wading, face upstream leaning into the current while moving sideways across the stream. A sturdy stick about 2 metres long will help you keep your balance in streams with a rocky or slippery bottom. The best method of keeping yourself upright, however, is to keep a firm hold of a handline. This can be taken across the river by one of your stronger swimmers, swimming in the minimum of clothing and attached to a lifeline. Everyone else can then wade across, wearing all their equipment. If wading is not possible, improvise flotation aids.

Airtight bag

Perhaps the most useful and practical method is to use your poncho (or any sheet of waterproof material), tie it at both ends and make an airtight bag, with your equipment inside, which will support both you and your equipment.

All this hassle and effort can, of course, be avoided if helicopters are available and if the operational situation permits their use. Clearly an enemy bank bristling with troops and anti-aircraft systems would almost certainly make helicopters a non-starter, but a surprise landing on the opposite bank against a relatively weak opposition is a much easier way of crossing a river than either by boat

Below: The Israelis bridge the Suez Canal using floating pontoons. Each pontoon is a separate vehicle: if you have not got enough elements, you can use it as a ferry.

Marines on Operation Harvest Moon in Vietnam keep their fighting order and M14s dry on a makeshift raft. In this situation you need one foot on the ground all the time, so cross in pairs with the rest covering.

SWIMMING

A jungle river crossing in Belize: it may look easy, but it is sometimes difficult to estimate how deep and fast-flowing these streams are. Native bridges may be washed away by the monsoon.

GATHERING RIVER INTELLIGENCE

River crossing operations must be planned as far in advance as possible. The primary planning factors are the river, the ground and the enemy. To succeed, you need up-to-date, accurate information on all three topics, but before you risk lives on recce patrol, you can gather intelligence in the following ways:

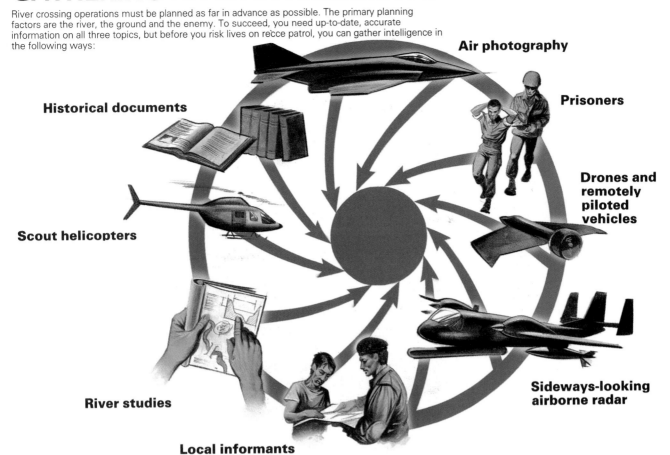

Air photography

Prisoners

Historical documents

Drones and remotely piloted vehicles

Scout helicopters

Sideways-looking airborne radar

River studies

Local informants

ACROSS

This man has been dragged under by the current and the weight of his equipment, and is exhausted and drowning. Another patrol member, a strong swimmer, is attempting a rescue.

A very close-run thing: there will always be soldiers who can't swim or are poor swimmers. They will not tell you this, so test them before you take them out into the field.

or swimming. Anti-tank helicopters can also be used to provide defence in the bridgehead.

River crossing at battalion level and above is a complex business involving waiting areas, check points, forming-up places, crossing sites and much more. At platoon level, you should concentrate on the business of getting across the river either in a boat, wading or swimming. Do this as silently as possible to take the enemy by surprise, and if you are compromised proceed as quickly as possible and with the maximum of fire support. Once you have established a bridgehead, the sappers can put reinforcements across by bridge or ferry. But if you fail, the operation must be called off.

The French PAA self-propelled bridge system. Once you have established the bridgehead, the sappers can put reinforcements across by bridge or ferry using one of these systems. Unfortunately, all bridging is very vulnerable to attack.

Combat Report
Angola:
Cross-Border Operation

A member of the Headquarters staff of the South African Parachute Brigade describes a cross-border operation with Pathfinder Company.

The Pathfinder Unit was a small but effective raiding force used on special operations against the terrorist organisation SWAPO (South West African People's Organisation), which operated from inside Angola against civilian and military personnel in SWA.

I was called to the area headquarters in Ishikati, the main base in northern SWA, about 100 kilometres south of the border with Angola. I received orders for a two-fold mission, to be carried out within seven days. We were to ambush the main culvert bridge between Ongina and Fangua, part of the only tarmac road in that area of Angola and the main communication and supply route for SWAPO. When a convoy passed we were to destroy the bridge with explosives and capture the equipment or personnel, and obtain intelligence on the location of any Soviet or Cuban troops and advisers in the area.

Time-consuming detours

The raiding group was to consist of five vehicles: two Jackal gunships, one 1.5-tonne Unimog with a 14.5-mm heavy machine-gun, and two 2.5-tonne Unimogs to carry demolition kit and support troops.

Having made our plan, we prepared about 150 kg of explosive in metal boxes, to be placed under the culverts. The latest intelligence reports indicated that enemy movement took place between midnight and 0500 hours. We practised for three days so that everyone knew exactly what they were supposed to do. First in the column was a Jackal, followed by the two larger Unimogs. Then came the small Unimog with the 14.5 heavy machine-gun and then, covering the rear, was the second Jackal.

We packed our equipment and moved to a position just inside the 'cut line', as the border with Angola was known. Here we linked up with guides from the local resistance movement in Angola. They took us to our staging point, about 30 km inside the border.

Once there, we went over our maps and photographs for the last time before setting off to cover the 120 km of enemy territory to our target. We moved at night, but it was difficult as

The plan was for the column to cross into Angola and make for the target which was 100 miles deep in enemy territory, moving at night to avoid detection.

the area was flat and featureless and full of native kraals. These kraals were surrounded by wooden cattle fences, which resisted even the most determined vehicles. This meant time-consuming detours.

At about 2200 hours, one of the sharp tree stumps left by the fence-makers ripped the petrol tank off one of the Unimogs. The convoy took up defensive positions as we tried to repair the damage. Suddenly shots were fired nearby and returned from other positions. The enemy's patrol were trying to locate us.

I realised that we were in a tricky situation, and decided to take a calculated risk. We turned our lights on and made as much noise as possible in the hope that they would take us for Angolan army soldiers. It worked, and we fixed the vehicle and went on our way.

As we neared our objective, it was lights off and back into the silent routine. Once at the bridge I sent a Jackal down the road in each direction so that they could warn of any advancing vehicles. Then the demolition party and their boxes of explosives went into the culverts. The tunnels under the road had high ceilings and the explosives had to be positioned right against the roof.

While the demolition party was working, the rest of us established our fire positions. The 60-mm mortar was sited and Claymores were positioned to fire along the flanks of the ambush. Once everything was in place, I recalled the Jackals and they positioned themselves to give cover.

We blew the charges

Then came a long and uncomfortable wait. Forty-five minutes before we were due to withdraw, our patience was rewarded by the growl of heavy vehicles approaching from the north. This was confirmed by our early warning team, positioned about 50 metres away and armed with RPG-7 grenade launchers. Suddenly out of the darkness loomed three Soviet GAZ 4+4 vehicles. They drove straight into the ambush. When the second one was squarely on the centre culvert, we blew the charges.

What a noise! We lay there stunned as the bush echoed around us. Then our machine-guns opened up and the mortar team lobbed flares into the sky, turning night into day.

There was no response from the smoking pile that was all that remained of the convoy, so the search teams were moved in to check for prisoners and any intelligence material.

"Nothing here, Boss," came the clipped radio message.

It was time to go. My main worry was the enemy armoured vehicles based in Ongina, 25 km away. The Angolan army, which supported SWAPO, had Cuban-manned BTR-60s and BRDM-2s, which easily outgunned our small force. Before we left, though, we had one final task. We laid several PMN anti-personnel mines, captured from a SWAPO team. We were returning them to their owners! Our mine-laying was interrupted by the distinctive sound of mortars nearby – and they weren't ours. The enemy was closing in.

Dawn had arrived, so we drove as quickly as possible towards the cut-line. Our route took us between the suspected locations of two Angolan army outposts. As our orders were not to engage them unless attacked, we moved as silently as possible.

The tension eased

The sentries must have seen us, because we suddenly began to receive fire. The gunner on our 14.5 fired half a dozen HEI (high explosive incendiary) rounds into the bush, and the firing ceased abruptly. Behind us the mortars were still exploring our last position but, more disturbingly, we could hear the distinctive rumble of armoured vehicles off to one side. It is very difficult to locate vehicles in the bush from their noise, so I hoped we weren't going to be outmanoeuvred.

Fortunately we were now entering the area dominated by the resistance forces. The Angolan army and SWAPO were unlikely to follow us here. The tension eased and everyone relaxed a little. We entered the small camp that had been our starting point. After embraces all round, we continued our journey and crossed into SWA at about midday. There was still the threat of mines here, but at least we didn't have to worry about running into any of the squat, ugly Soviet armour that had been pursuing us.

Back at base I briefed the intelligence major and gave him the material we had retrieved. The most interesting item was a Cuban NCO's notebook giving details of demolition training, which confirmed their presence in Ongina. The intelligence officer told me that radio intercept had picked up details of our raid, and SWAPO had lost six men and three trucks filled with supplies and radio spares. Later that week, we received aerial photographs which showed that the road had been completely destroyed. Another success for the Pathfinders!

A Jackal 'gunship', one of the improvised troop carriers used by South Africa in the early 1980s.

Combat Skills

CALLING IN THE WRATH OF GOD

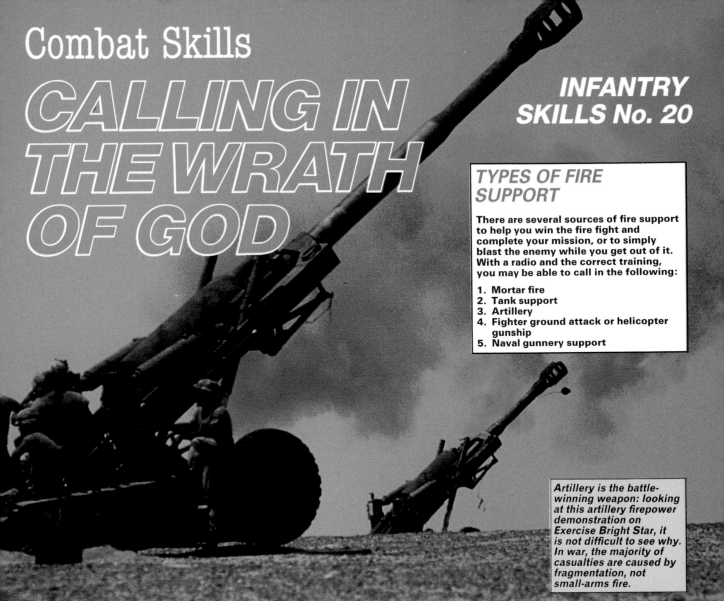

TYPES OF FIRE SUPPORT

There are several sources of fire support to help you win the fire fight and complete your mission, or to simply blast the enemy while you get out of it. With a radio and the correct training, you may be able to call in the following:

1. Mortar fire
2. Tank support
3. Artillery
4. Fighter ground attack or helicopter gunship
5. Naval gunnery support

Artillery is the battle-winning weapon: looking at this artillery firepower demonstration on Exercise Bright Star, it is not difficult to see why. In war, the majority of casualties are caused by fragmentation, not small-arms fire.

CALLING IN A FIRE MISSION

Infantry units will not usually be without some form of fire support. If you get into any trouble, the most likely source of help is your own mortar platoon.

Each mortar section is allotted two mortar fire controllers, and occasionally an MFC will go with you for a specific operation; but do not assume they will always be there. In the ideal world, everyone should be able to pick up a radio and call in fire support: platoon and section commanders are not bullet proof and the ability to get artillery or mortar rounds onto the enemy with speed and accuracy is the way to avoid the body bag.

In the Vietnam War, fortified fire support bases protected patrols out on search-and-destroy missions. If a unit came under contact, the way to win the firefight was by artillery or air strike. Unfortunately, some of the terrain in Vietnam limited the effect of such fire superiority. The rather worried platoon leader on the right is calling in some fire on a suspected VC position prior to assaulting it.

Terrain and weather conditions in the jungle do not favour good comms; it is often very difficult to achieve line of sight. If you cannot contact your fire support, try to contact any station on your radio net and get them to relay the message. This way you can greatly increase your range.

Artillery target indication is the procedure used by infantrymen to engage targets quickly and effectively with artillery fire. If there is an artillery Forward Observation Officer (FOO) with you, he will call for artillery fire using slightly different procedures, but there are never enough FOOs to be everywhere all the time, so you will often have to call for your own artillery support.

Sometimes an artillery officer in your battle group will be able to take over the fire mission once he has identified the target, but more often than not you will have to complete the entire engagement, and, when you are working as an independent section or platoon, there will be no gunner in the area anyway.

A fire mission is divided into three phases: the **initial orders**, the **adjust-**ment of fire phase, and **fire for effect**.

The **initial order** gives all the essential information to the gun line for them to lay the guns onto the target indicated by you. First you must call the artillery OP officer who is supporting you – you will know his callsign on your radio net – and alert him to the fact that you require artillery support by saying "Fire Mission, over". He will answer you by repeating "Fire

High Explosive Fire

The artillery can vary the fall of their shells to suit the target. The main types are:

1 Simple concentration

The fastest and easiest to lay onto an area target: the grid reference you give them should indicate the centre of the target. The spread of fire around a point target for the Abbot 155-mm would be:

50×100 m (using three guns)
150×150 m (using a battery – eight guns)
250×250 m (using a regiment – three batteries)

2 Linear concentration

Here the shells fall in a line along a given bearing. A regiment of 18 guns can blast a 500-metre long strip in this way.

3 Airburst

HE shells in either simple or linear concentratio can be detonated in the air using controlled variable time fuses (CVT) or proximity burst fuses. The optimal burst height is about 10 metres. Airburst is extremely effective against troops in the open and those without overhead protection.

The 105-mm Light Gun L118 is shown here in service with the Royal Artillery. It will throw a shell out to 17km. The safe splinter distance – the closest you should consider calling it in near you – is 250 metres for an HE shell for observed fire.

The infantry's artillery: the 81-mm mortar. Talking to the mortars is usually the fastest way to get rounds on the ground; the rate of fire is substantial. Maximum effective range for HE is 5800 metres; safe splinter distance is 300 metres.

Mission, over". This is the signal for you to tell him:

1 Where the target is
2 The direction of the target from your position
3 What the target is
4 What you want done about it
5 When you want fire support, and how long for

You indicate **where the target is** by giving a six-figure grid reference, or you can refer to a previously registered target and adjust from it, for instance "Reference ZW 4831, left 200". This refers his guns to a target which they already have on their computer and which has been allocated the target number ZW 4831 and tells them to fire 200 metres to the left of it. Alternatively you can fire tracer or mortar smoke rounds at the target, but this is only in a situation where the FOO can see the target and when you are attempting to hand over the engagement to him.

Direction of target

For the guns to be able to make sense of your adjustments, they must know the **direction of the target from your position**. You calculate this by taking a bearing with your compass on the target. This will give you a magnetic bearing; unless you convert it to a grid bearing, you should specify that you are sending a magnetic bearing.

North Vietnamese regulars equipped with Russian D-74 122-mm field guns, in typical Soviet line formation, fire in support of their troops advancing on South Vietnamese units in Quang Tri province, 1972.

moke

n excellent way of neutralising the enemy, or
least reducing the effectiveness of his direct
e while you move. Again, you can have simple
linear concentration:

Simple concentration

simple smoke shoot usually consists of three
ns firing smoke instead of HE.

Linear concentration

is produces the deliberate smoke screen. An
obot 105-mm gun section can produce a
nokescreen 600 metres long lasting for about
ght minutes with its first-line scales of ammo.
Smoke rounds can also be very handy for
prrecting artillery fire where you are having
buble observing the burst, e.g. in the jungle.
bloured smoke rounds are used for indicating
rgets to ground attack aircraft.

luminating rounds

bu can turn night into day for limited periods:
e 105-mm round illuminates a circle of
)0-metre diameter for 30 seconds. The
55-mm round will illuminate a 1600-metre
rcle for 75 seconds.

*This massive beast is the US M110
203-mm gun. Artillery pieces of this size
are usually corps or divisional assets, so
you won't often have this in support.*

So you will say, for instance, "Direction 1620 magnetic".

Next you must say **what the target is.** You must be as precise as possible so that the guns can choose the correct ammunition, allocate priorities and decide on the amount of ammunition necessary to neutralise that particular target. Therefore you must give some sort of description such as "Infantry platoon advancing across open ground," or "mortar platoon now firing from left hand edge of fir wood," or "tanks refuelling in clearing".

Fire options

The next piece of information that is required by the guns is **what you want done about the target.** Your options

are to neutralise, smoke off, or destroy it. In the vast majority of cases too much time and ammunition is required to physically destroy a target. Instead you can ask for a smoke fire mission to mask a move by your troops, for instance to enable them to manoeuvre across relatively open countryside to get into a position to mount an assault.

Smoke is also used to frustrate enemy intentions. If you are being threatened by enemy direct or indirect fire, it may help to obscure his line of sight and will slow him down even if he has the most sophisticated thermal imaging devices, which can "see through" smoke.

The most usual order, however, is

"neutralise". This means that sufficient fire must be brought to bear to render the target ineffective in the current battle. Even tanks can be neutralised by artillery fire if their optics and radio antennae are damaged.

Pick your time

Lastly the guns will need to know **when** you want them to fire and for **how long.** You have various options: you can simply order "Now," or "For x minutes," or "For x minutes at y hours". Alternatively you can order the guns to "Report when ready". So your final fire order might sound something like this:

No. 2 Section Commander: "Hello G11, this is I12, fire mission, over."

CALLING IN ARTILLERY FIRE AND SENDING CORRECTIONS

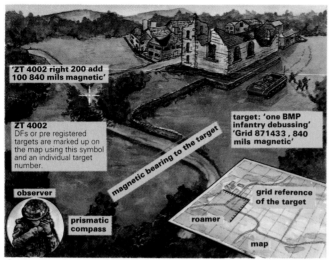

'ZT 4002 right 200 add 100 840 mils magnetic'

ZT 4002
DFs or pre registered targets are marked up on the map using this symbol and an individual target number.

target: 'one BMP infantry debussing' 'Grid 871433 , 840 mils magnetic'

observer

prismatic compass

magnetic bearing to the target

roamer

grid reference of the target

map

Gathering the information

In any phase of war it is a good idea to keep constant track of where you are on the map, so if you do come under contact you can send accurate grid references quickly for contact reports and fire missions. When calling for artillery, always engage the brain before putting the mouth into gear. You need your map and a prismatic compass. From the map, work out exactly where you are and where the enemy is, and use the prismatic to get the magnetic bearing from you to the target.

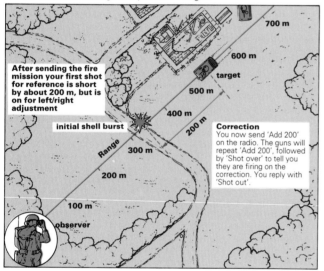

700 m

600 m

target

500 m

400 m

After sending the fire mission your first shot for reference is short by about 200 m, but is on for left/right adjustment

initial shell burst

Range

300 m

200 m

100 m

observer

Correction
You now send 'Add 200' on the radio. The guns will repeat 'Add 200', followed by 'Shot over' to tell you they are firing on the correction. You reply with 'Shot out'.

Range correction (1)

Imagine a line drawn from you to the target. Rounds short or long are corrected using the words 'add' or 'drop' the appropriate number of metres. It is always better to over-correct so that you bracket the target. Correction is normally 400 metres or 200 metres.

Military binocular graticules

The Army measures angles in mils, not degrees. There are 6400 mils to 360 degrees.

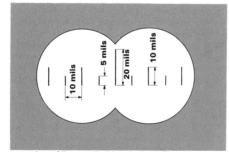

10 mils

5 mils

20 mils

10 mils

Military binoculars have a series of lines called 'graticules'. They are used to judge range and measure the left/right error in artillery target indication. Each small division equals 10 mils; one mil subtends 1 metre at 1000 metres. Look through the binos and measure the distance between the burst and the target as 30 mils: if the target is 1000 metres away, the correction is 30 metres right or left; if the target is 2000 metres away, the correction is 60 metres.

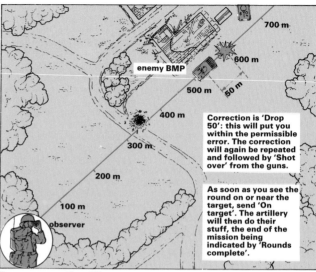

700 m

600 m

enemy BMP

500 m

50 m

400 m

300 m

Correction is 'Drop 50': this will put you within the permissible error. The correction will again be repeated and followed by 'Shot over' from the guns.

200 m

As soon as you see the round on or near the target, send 'On target'. The artillery will then do their stuff, the end of the mission being indicated by 'Rounds complete'.

100 m

observer

Range correction (2)

If the Forward Observation Officer cannot see the target you will have to send corrections. When you hear him say 'Shot over' on the radio, watch carefully for the impact of the round. Corrections must be sent quickly as the enemy will not usually sit still for a shelling. Make sure you do not call down fire too close to your own troops.

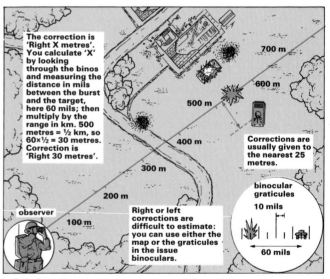

The correction is 'Right X metres'. You calculate 'X' by looking through the binos and measuring the distance in mils between the burst and the target, here 60 mils; then multiply by the range in km. 500 metres = ½ km, so 60×½ = 30 metres. Correction is 'Right 30 metres'.

700 m

600 m

500 m

400 m

Corrections are usually given to the nearest 25 metres.

300 m

binocular graticules

10 mils

observer

200 m

100 m

Right or left corrections are difficult to estimate: you can use either the map or the graticules in the issue binoculars.

60 mils

Left/right adjustment

This is always difficult to guesstimate, so don't. Measure the error using the binos and convert to find the error in metres right or left of the target. Use the words 'left' and 'right', and correct down to 25 metres of the target.

HAND ANGLES

Note: This is a rough guide for the average hand. Where possible, use binos or the map.

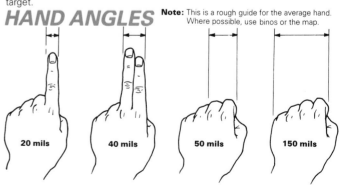

20 mils

40 mils

50 mils

150 mils

If you have no binoculars, you can use your hand at arm's length as a rough guide. The conversion from mils to the actual correction you send to the guns may seem complicated, but you only need to reach for the pocket calculator if the numbers are awkward. All you are doing is multiplying the correction in mils by the range to the target in kilometres.

CALLING IN THE WRATH OF GOD

OP Officer: "G11, fire mission, over."

No. 2 Section Commander: "I12, Grid 834629, direction one seven eight zero magnetic, enemy platoon debussing from APCs, neutralise for three minutes, report when ready, over."

OP Officer: "G11, Grid 834629, direction one seven eight zero magnetic, enemy platoon debussing from APCs, neutralise for three minutes, report when ready, wait out."

At this stage the OP officer will attempt to identify the target. If he does so, your job is over. But if he can't, as will often be the case, he will ask you to send corrections: this is the **adjustment of fire** phase.

Fire for effect

Once the guns are on target, they will produce the type and amount of fire that you requested in your initial order. In other words, they will **fire for effect**. You can continue to correct the fire if you consider that it has been ineffective, but if you are satisfied, you should order "End of Mission". Alternatively you can order "Repeat" or request a further number of minutes' fire. Finally, if you think that a target may re-appear at the same spot again, ask the guns to record the target. This means that the same target can be engaged very quickly without adjustment of fire at some future time.

Logical process

Calling in fire missions can seem a daunting business. Don't allow the procedures to confuse you; it is straightforward and logical and gets much easier with practice. If you are doubtful about the correct sequence of orders, tell your gunner what you want him to do in basic English and he will produce the answer. But you must be able to give him a six-figure grid reference of the target and a magnetic bearing to it from your position.

A moment's notice

Artillery target indication procedure is the same for all mortars and guns, whatever their type or calibre. Once you have mastered the procedures you can be confident that you can call up artillery support at a moment's notice — an encouraging thought when you are in a front-line slit trench armed only with an SA80 and faced with a Soviet Motor Rifle Battalion!

A US Army combat control team in the Egyptian desert on Exercise Bright Star discusses the DF tasks to cover the approaches to their position. These DFs are pre-registered artillery targets. If you pre-register a target with the guns, all you have to do is shout the target number down the radio to get rounds on the ground.

Artillery assets are always in short supply on the modern battlefield (unless of course you are a member of Group Soviet Forces Germany), so you cannot rely on the guns supporting you unless they are on priority call to you or in direct support.

You must give an accurate description of the target so that the gunners can decide what type of ammo to use. Infantry in the open, like this, are best taken out with airburst munitions (proximity fused), but for those dug in deep or in APCs contact-detonated or time-delay ammo may be more suitable. Make sure the gunner has enough information to make the right decision.

Combat Report

Togo:
Replacing the President

A British mercenary in Togo is involved in a plot to overthrow the president and replace him with a new head of government. It turned out that others had the same idea.

Togo is a small West African state bordered by the far larger countries of Ghana and Dahomey. From the late 1960s to the mid 1970s mercenary involvement was extensive throughout Africa. Governments were toppled many times in the course of a year; one African state is recorded to have at least 20 different presidents in the span of five years.

My involvement in Togo began in the summer of 1977 after being approached by some mercenary friends who told me that there was a contract in Africa. The operation was to overthrow President Eyadema and escort the new head of government to the presidential palace. There was expected to be minimum opposition and the main mercenary element would only consist of nine men. Infiltrating the country by air, we were to RV with members of the Togolese Liberation Army who had the necessary plans and weapons stashed away. The operation was bankrolled by the son of a former president of the country who made his money from his sugar plantations in Ivory Coast.

Most of us expected to spend a few days lying low before RV'ing with the TLA, and if all went well we could be basking in the sun drinking cold beers within the week. Although the plan was simple and there was little opposition we had no way of knowing that three other mercenary operations, each with a different president to put in power, were being planned. All three were scheduled to take place at the same time! Naturally each separate group and its financiers did not know that a similar operation had been planned.

A final recce

After spending a few days in Togo drinking lukewarm beer we met up with elements of the TLA, who took us to a small village near the border of Ghana. The weapons had been buried but no-one had thought to wrap them in protective covering. They had simply been thrown into the bottom of a hole and soil thrown on top. The seven Sterling SMGs, number 36 grenades and a Carl Gustav 84-mm antitank gun with a dented venturi all required a complete strip-down and clean.

The weapons were in such an appalling state that it took several hours to clean and oil them before starting to remove rust from the inside of the barrels and working parts. Later examination revealed that one of the Sterlings had extensive damage inside the barrel. This weapon was later discarded. The ammunition was also in a similar state and most of it had to be cleaned in petrol. The following day a senior member of the TLA gave us hand-drawn sketches of the presidential palace, neighbouring streets and details of where a car would be found ready for an immediate getaway after bundling the president in the back. We also received confirmation that twenty mercenaries in neighbouring Ghana were ready to escort the new president to the palace. All that needed to be done now was a final recce of the palace and surrounding vicinity so we could match the physical features of the area with that of the maps and drawing which had been supplied to us.

Walking openly past the palace, we looked like just another group of western tourists. We noticed that the so-called 'palace guards' were a disorganised rabble. Some were asleep with their weapons, mainly Soviet SKSs, lying up against the wall. Others openly played cards. Even the soldiers who were carrying their weapons tended to carry them over their shoulders, holding them by the barrel. On our return to the lying-up point we did a last minute weapons check and once again talked through our plan of attack to ensure that each man knew what he was to do. The essence of the operation was stealth and speed, followed by a quick dash towards the border with the president in the back of the car.

On seeing us he froze

We now set off after discarding our civilian clothes and wearing OG and armed with Sterlings. We were only about one mile from the objective when we stumbled across a patrol, face to face. We just stared at one another because they were also Europeans. While my men covered me, I met the leader of the other patrol in no-man's land. The other mercenaries were French and they were on their way to abduct the president as well. After establishing that both patrols were on the same side even though we had two different men to place in power, we all got together, exchanged cigarettes and started to talk the problem over. We agreed that we could both launch an attack simultaneously but we were going to have problems when two different potential presidents arrived on the scene!

The situation was so unbelievable that for a while we discussed the French para wings that the French mercenaries were wearing before telling them of our previous military units. How about if we mounted a joint operation, abducted the president and made for the safety of Ghana before clearing off and letting the two separate rebel forces sort out the problem, I said to the French commander. Suddenly there was the loud rustle of branches as a European burst through a clump of trees near where we were sitting. On seeing us he froze. I said to the French commander: 'How many men have you got out there?' Giving me a startled look, he said, 'I assumed he was one of yours.'

'Damn it, what the hell's going on here?' said a loud voice.

The mercenary mumbled something in French.

The mercenary was immediately bombarded with questions in French and English and he replied in broken English that he was a Belgian. 'Bloody Belgium: what are you doing here?'

Training before the operation, we had decent weapons. No-one told us that when it came to the real thing we'd get wartime relics instead.

one of the lads shouted.

'Abducting the president,' he said.

I shook my head in disbelief and the French commander held his head in his hands. We were in one of the smallest and poorest African states, a country so small that very few people knew of its existence. On the same day and same place there were three separate mercenary operations taking place for the benefit of three separate presidents in exile.

A gruesome end

After asking the Belgian further questions, we found out that he was a member of a ten man team that had walked directly into an ambush. He was the only one to escape; the others had been taken prisoner. In his opinion the enemy had been tipped off. The decision to bug out and make for the safety of Ghana was agreed upon by all. It was several years before we discovered that the Belgian mercenaries who were captured were hanged and their heads later placed on spears and displayed outside the palace until they rotted.

Government troops were armed with a mixture of weapons and their gun handling was very poor.

Combat Skills

WORKING WITH TANKS

In most combat situations, tanks and infantry are indispensable to each other: each can fulfil certain tasks that the other cannot.
Tanks are more suited to operating in open countryside, where they can engage targets at long range; but infantry prefer urban or wooded areas, where they are less vulnerable and where their shorter-range weapons are more effective.

Tanks can cover infantry while they are in the open, and infantry can protect tanks while they are at their most vulnerable from close-range ambush in wooded or built-up areas. So you and your supporting tanks must know how to work closely together.

Sometimes you will want to direct each other's fire onto enemy targets. Usually it will be you, the infantry commander, who will want to direct tank fire onto targets that are obstructing your advance or causing casualties to your men. You may, for instance, be finding it hard to neutralise a well dug-in machine-gun. Tanks will often spot such targets before you do, and engage them without your guidance. You, of course, can do the same for the

TASKS FOR TANKS AND INFANTRY

These are the tasks an armour heavy battlegroup would be expected to take on. 'Armour heavy' simply means that there are two squadrons of tanks and one company of infantry.

1. Rapid advance to contact with the enemy, or following up a deliberate withdrawal.
2. Assault and destruction of enemy defended positions.
3. Exploitation of weaknesses in the enemy front line, penetration and pursuit.
4. Counter-attack and counter-penetration.
5. Aggressive reconnaissance by day and night.
6. Diversionary operations and flank protection.
7. Screening or covering force operations protecting the main defensive position and/or buying time for its completion.

An M67 flamethrowing tank of the US Marine Corps suppresses an area suspected of containing a VC sniper. A tank's massive firepower is the result of the combination of fire from main armament and machine guns. Correct use of tank support once in contact will minimise your infantry casualties. In return, you must protect the tanks from enemy anti-tank weapons.

Tanks are great for cracking hard pinpoint targets like bunkers, other tanks and APCs. These US Marines are using an M48 to engage a well dug-in NVA position. American use of armour in close country in Vietnam was surprisingly effective.

Austrian infantry charges past a knocked-out tank on exercise. Armour is extremely vulnerable in close country without adequate infantry protection. In war, keep away from tank hulks: the ammo may cook off, and they tend to draw fire.

tanks by dealing with anti-tank weapons. But if a target has not been spotted by you or your supporting tanks, you must have a method of indicating targets to each other.

Quick transmission

Usually you will need to transmit your message quickly, so you cannot use the slow and complicated Target Grid Procedure. Similarly, you cannot use smoke since there is likely to be a lot about already, and anyway it might obscure the target.

So how do you talk to a tank commander? Basically, you have three choices: by radio, by tank telephone or by personal contact. Each method has advantages in different circumstances. The best is personal contact

ARMOUR AND INFANTRY COOPERATION

The roles of armour and infantry although different, are complementary. Tanks are suitable for some tasks, and infantry for others; in order to get the best results each must know the other's capabilities and limitations. Armour and infantry usually work closely together, and the ratio of tanks and infantry is varied according to the task in hand. For example, in attack you need more tanks; in defence, you need more infantry.

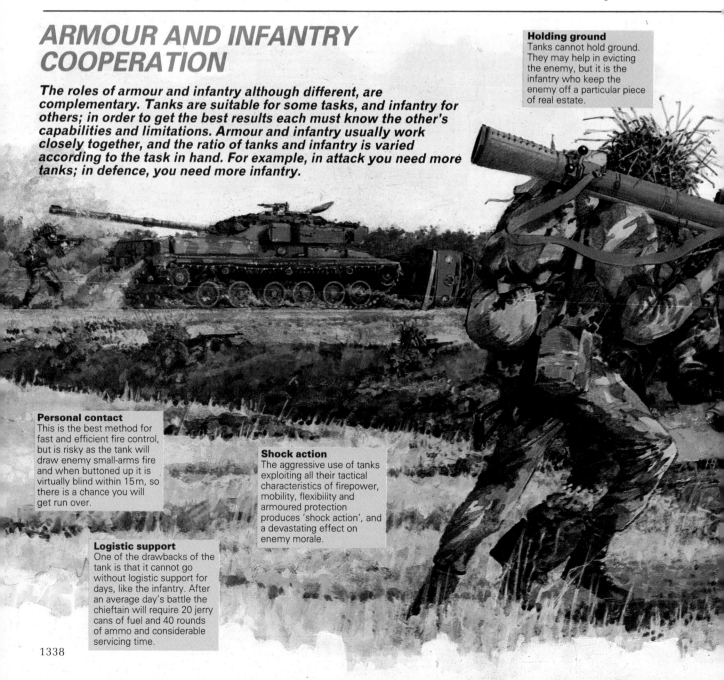

Holding ground
Tanks cannot hold ground. They may help in evicting the enemy, but it is the infantry who keep the enemy off a particular piece of real estate.

Personal contact
This is the best method for fast and efficient fire control, but is risky as the tank will draw enemy small-arms fire and when buttoned up it is virtually blind within 15m, so there is a chance you will get run over.

Shock action
The aggressive use of tanks exploiting all their tactical characteristics of firepower, mobility, flexibility and armoured protection produces 'shock action', and a devastating effect on enemy morale.

Logistic support
One of the drawbacks of the tank is that it cannot go without logistic support for days, like the infantry. After an average day's battle the chieftain will require 20 jerry cans of fuel and 40 rounds of ammo and considerable servicing time.

This is tank country. Here the infantry is very vulnerable without the tank support. Tanks and infantry usually fight together in mixed units made up of differing combinations called company squadron groups.

but, as this usually requires you to climb onto the tank, it is not always advisable. So usually you have to use the radio or the tank telephone.

Both the Chieftain and Challenger Main Battle Tanks have a small box attached to the rear with a telephone that connects you to the tank commander. Being situated at the back of the tank, you are automatically covered, but make sure that the driver is not about to put the tank into reverse!

Call sign

If you have to use the radio you will need to know the call sign of the tank you want to talk to: this will be painted on its turret or hull.

Within each squadron there are four

Battalions in Germany no longer fight as separate units but as the 'all arms' battlegroup made up of tanks, infantry, engineers, signals, REME support and dedicated artillery. This is a company squadron group of Chieftains and APCs.

Night vision devices and optics
Modern tanks have excellent night fighting devices and optics which can be used to identify infantry targets. Do not forget the searchlight, which may also be of use in the right tactical situation.

Surprise
The size, weight and noise of the main battle tank may make surprise difficult to achieve. However, good forward planning, for example covering the noise of movement with artillery and smoke, may solve the problem.

Sensitivity to ground
Unlike infantry, tanks have problems crossing boggy or rocky ground, and steep slopes, thick mature woodland, rivers and minefields are effective barriers.

Tank telephone
Most tanks are fitted with a tank telephone on the outside rear of the tank, but most crews have ripped them out to discourage the infantry using them (there have been some nasty accidents on exercise).

Radio
This is the usual method of communication, and the safest as you can keep your distance.

Indicating targets to tanks

When you are working with tanks rather than artillery you have to be in contact with the individual tank commander who controls the gun fire. Once the tank is buttoned up it has limited vision, so you must be its eyes and ears: spotting targets, giving target indications and advising the type and duration of fire.

There are several methods of indication:

1 Reference point method

This works in the same way as giving fire control orders to a section. The platoon or section commander spots a target and requests help from a supporting tank on the radio. The tank is operating on the same radio frequency as the infantry radio net and is called using the individual tank's callsign, which in this case is Tango One Three. The platoon commander's callsign is India One One Alpha.

Inf: "Hullo T13, this is I11A, target, over"

Tank: "T13, send, over". The tank commander is ready to receive the message, in this case the target information.

Inf: "I11A, lone tree [a reference point briefed to all at the end of the last tactical bound], **go right four o'clock** [the infantryman is using the clock ray method to indicate to the tank commander where the enemy is], **400** [range in metres to the actual target], **machine-gun in hedgerow** [you must tell the tank commander what he is looking for so he can identify it and select the right type of ammo], **destroy** [this is what you want done to the target], **over."**

Tank: "T13, wilco, out".
"Wilco" stands for "will comply", which means the order is understood and will be actioned. Watch out for fall of shot as he is about to plaster the target with machine-gun fire and a splash of HE to complete the job.

2 Gun barrel method

To use this method you tell the gunner where the tank gun is pointing in relation to the target.

Inf: "Hullo T13, this is I11A, target, over."

Tank: "T13, send, over."

Inf: "I11A, gun barrel [method of indication of target], **quarter right** [move the gun barrel right through 45 degrees], **800** [the range to the target], **small copse, identify, over."**
The target is well camouflaged and difficult to see, so the infantry commander gives the indication in two halves, enabling the tank to use its excellent optics to positively identify the target.

Tank: "T13, identified, over."
The tank commander swings the turret quarter right and looks over the gun barrel at 800 m for the copse. If he cannot see the copse then he reports "Not seen", and the infantry sends another indication.

Inf: "I11A from copse, right, four o'clock, enemy bunker, neutralise and cease fire on my order, over."

Tank: "T13, wilco, out."

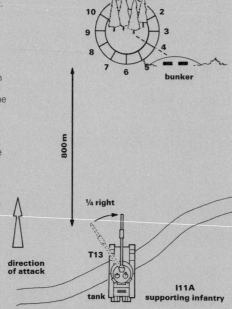

3 Burst for reference fired by the tank

Where a target is particularly difficult to indicate, ask the tank to fire a burst from its maching-gun in the general direction of the target and then correct by watching where the burst goes.

Inf: "Hullo T13, this is I11A, target, over."

Tank: "T13, send, over."

Inf: "I11A, gun barrel, quarter left, 600, fire burst for reference, over."

Tank: "T13, wilco, wait out."
You will have to wait while he identifies the target.

Tank: "I11A, this is T13, shot out."
This warns the infantry to look out for the burst he is about to fire to note where it lands.

Inf: "Hullo T13, this is I11A, from last burst right 100 drop 50, enemy in bunker, neutralise, I am attacking left flank, over."
This corrects the tank machine-gun fire onto the target and warns the tank to expect them to attack the position from the left. When the infantry are almost on the enemy, the infantry would call for rapid fire as the assault goes in and would then tell the tank to switch fire to targets in depth when the infantry have reached the bunker.

Tank: "T13, wilco, out."
The tank will fire at a steady rate, keeping the enemy's heads down and conserving ammo as the infantry approach their FUP for the attack. Then, as they assault, the tank will fire longer bursts to suppress the bunker as the infantry move to grenade or satchel charge posting distance.

troops of tanks, and within each troop there are four tanks. 'A' Squadron's call sign is 1, 'B' Squadron's 2 and so on. So the 2nd Troop leader in 'A' Squadron will be 12. His Troop Sergeant's tank will be 12A, and the other two tanks commanded by Corporals will be 12B and 12C. So immediately you look at the tanks you can tell which tank he is in and which troop and squadron he belongs to.

Once you have attracted the tank commander's attention, direct his attention to the target. You have three ways of doing this.

Reference points

First, you can use reference points. If possible, arrange these before an operation. You must select them by looking at the battleground and not from a map. Choose clearly defined features that will leave no room for confusion.

You can use your chosen reference points to guide the tank commander's eyes from it to the target via a succession of landmarks using the clockface method.

If you cannot use the reference point method, the tank gun barrel can be used as a datum line instead. You will normally be able to see the direction of the gun barrel, and so you can guide it 'quarter RIGHT' or 'half LEFT' onto the target. This is a simple but effective method that requires no planning before an operation.

If it is impossible to use either of these methods, you can use the burst of a shell from a tank, or the strike and tracer from an infantry or tank machine-gun, as a datum point from which corrections can be given. If you are going to use one of your machine-guns to mark a target, warn the tank commander when you are going to fire and also indicate the direction he must look in. He must do the same for you, if he is using his main armament or a machine-gun to indicate a target to you.

Fire correction

You can correct inaccurate fire. If the tank commander fails to identify the target or engages the wrong one, you can either give corrections from the fall of shot, or give another description of the correct target. You must give your corrections as if you were in the same position as the tank. Tell the tank commander to go the requisite number of metres LEFT or RIGHT or to 'add' or 'drop'. You cannot hope to control tank fire as you can artillery fire; your aim must be to direct the tank commander's eyes to the target. Highly sophisticated fire control equipment on the tank then enables the target to be engaged quickly and effectively.

Although the tank has the bigger punch and will often be useful in getting you out of difficult situations, when close country or a village or a town has to be negotiated it is you who will take the lead. You must ensure that no enemy infantry, with close-range anti-tank weapons, are lurking behind cover to take out your tanks.

Blind tanks

Remember, a tank is relatively blind when it comes to seeing the ground immediately around it. Its highly sophisticated sighting system is optimised to acquire targets at ranges up to 2,000 metres; there is little a tank can do if an infantryman manages to get within 100 metres with a close-range anti-tank weapon such as the RPG-7. So when you are moving through woods, or a built-up area, move ahead of your supporting tanks, clear the area of enemy, and then call up the tanks when it is safe for them to proceed. Remember, they can always give you fire support from their hull-down position to your rear while you are clearing ahead.

If you are working in APCs the tactics are different, but the principles

An M48 pumps 90-mm HE rounds into a VC position as Vietnamese marines prepared to assault during the Tet offensive. A tank used as a mobile strongpoint can definitively give you the edge in FIBUA.

remain the same. Even though you will cover ground more quickly it will still be the tanks' task to cover your vulnerable APCs across open ground, and it will be your job to dismount from your APCs and see the tanks and your empty APCs through close countryside.

Whether you are operating on foot or in APCs, close team work between tanks and infantry is absolutely vital. You both need each other, so get to know your opposite numbers in your supporting tanks.

Swedish troops debus to assault an objective supported by fire from their APCs and 'S' tanks. The tanks shoot them onto the objective and then switch fire to any positions in depth.

The Warsaw Pact have always recognised the importance of close co-operation between tanks and infantry, so their basic fighting unit is a mixture of mechanised infantry and tanks: either tank-heavy in the Tank Regiment, or infantry-heavy in the Motor Rifle Regiment.

STOPPAGES AND IMMEDIATE ACTION

The open-bolt SMG is a simple weapon that, provided the ammunition, gun and magazines are kept in good order, should not malfunction. If stoppages do occur, you will have a better idea of how to clear them and how to prevent them happening in the first place if you understand exactly how the weapon works. Remember, the SMG is used at close quarters so you must be able to deal with any problems very quickly.

Safety

In a weapon that fires from an open bolt, the actual cartridge case plays a very important part in safety, because it is the case that seals the chamber until the bullet has left the barrel and the pressure has dropped to a safe level. Note that the mechanical feeding of the round by the bolt from the magazine into the chamber is the only way to ensure the safe firing of the weapon. Therefore, in peacetime follow these rules:

1 Do not put damaged rounds back into a magazine.
2 Do not use any round involved in a stoppage, even if it appears undamaged.
3 Do not feed rounds into the chamber by hand, or fire rounds that are half-fed into the chamber.

4 Carefully check the magazine lips of all the magazines you are issued with. All damaged magazines must be discarded; they are the most common cause of accidents.
5 Always check that the magazine is fully seated in the magazine well or a dangerous stoppage may occur.
6 Always check that the barrel is clear before firing.
7 Check that the breech block is clean and is not corroded or cracked.

STOPPAGE IMMEDIATE ACTION
If your weapon stops firing, attempt to cock it. If you cannot, this is caused by a stuck case: remove the magazine, keeping the weapon pointing at the enemy. Then brace the weapon against your body, loop the sling over the cocking handle, and pull back hard to extract the case.

When filling the magazines, make sure you push the rounds right to the back of the mag. You should be able to fill a Sterling SMG mag with 34 rounds in less than 55 seconds (the magazine functions more reliably when filled with 28 rounds).

MAGAZINE STOPPAGE
If the weapon fails to fire when you first press the trigger, look inside after carrying out the IA. If you see rounds in the magazine but nothing in the chamber, push the base of the magazine firmly and continue firing. This stoppage is caused by the magazine not being fully seated in the magazine well.

FEEDWAY STOPPAGE
If you have a live round stuck in the chamber or on the feedway, you may be able to clear it when you cock the weapon by shaking the loose round out. If you can't shift it, apply the safety catch and remove the magazine. Put the safety catch at safe and prise or shake out the round or case. Check that the barrel is clear, and reload with a fresh magazine.

SEPARATED CASE
When you are in contact with the enemy you cannot afford to spend too much time clearing a stoppage: he could be less than 50 metres away. If you get a difficult stoppage or a separated case where the extractor has torn off the base of the round, it makes better sense to draw your pistol and carry on.

Weak charges

Poor quality ammunition can lead to problems. When the weapon is fired, either the percussion cap will fail to fire the main charge and simply push the bullet a little way up the barrel, or the charge does not completely burn on initiation, causing the same problem. If you fired another shot in this situation, you could be injured by a breech explosion. You must be able to recognise the signs of a weak charge, which are:

1 The sound of the weapon firing is quieter than usual.
2 The bolt stays forward and fails to eject the fired case.
3 When you cock the weapon to clear the stoppage an unusual amount of smoke comes out of the chamber.

STOVEPIPE
This type of stoppage will usually remedy itself as soon as you cock the weapon as this takes the pressure off the working parts and the empty case is free to fall away. In peacetime you must always remove the magazine and check the barrel clear.

ACTION IN CONTACT WITH THE ENEMY
The stoppage drills taught here are designed to put safety first. In war, you have to cope with the enemy and adopt a more realistic drill. It would be an acceptable risk to cock the weapon and fire a round to clear a round already stuck in the barrel. You can also fire rounds stuck in the chamber, and clear a stoppage by shaking out the round.

Direct blowback operation

1 Trigger release
When the weapon is cocked, the main spring is compressed and held back by the sear engaging a cut-out in the breech block. When the trigger is pressed the sear is pulled down, releasing the breech block, which is forced forward by the mainspring. Two horns on the face of the breech block pass each side of the ejector piece and hit the base of the top cartridge in the magazine, forcing it into the chamber. The breech block is still moving forward when the fixed firing pin strikes the percussion cap in the base of the round.

2 Cartridge ignition
The percussion cap fires, igniting the main charge, and the rapidly expanding gases from this force the bullet down the barrel. The explosion forces the bullet out and the breech block and cartridge case back. Because the breech block is still moving forward and weighs far more than the bullet it does not move back until the bullet has exited the barrel.

3 Case extraction
If the breech opens before the bullet leaves the barrel, the resultant breech explosion would cause pieces of the case and very hot gas to blow back in the firer's face. Damaged rounds or magazines can cause such an explosion. In the normal firing cycle the breech moves back with the case held in place by the extractor claw in the breech block.

4 Case ejection
The base of the round strikes the ejector piece, which tosses the case out to the right. The breech block has now passed over the sear, and when its rearward momentum is overcome by the pressure of the mainspring it will move forward until it is held by the sear engaging the cut-out, if the weapon is set for semi-automatic fire. If the weapon is on auto and the trigger still held back, the sear will stay down and the breech block will ride over it to chamber the next round and continue the firing cycle.

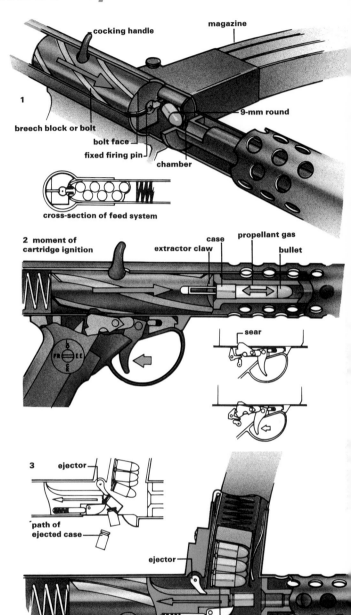
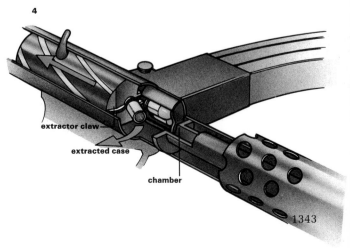

1343

THE CHEMICAL SAFETY RULE

The Immediate Action Drill

The enemy will try to achieve surprise to inflict maximum casualties with his chemical weapons. He can do this by mixing gas shells with conventional High Explosive or using delivery means that you cannot hear or see. The shell may burst at some distance from your position and the gas drift down to you. You must not wait to be told: use your own personal initiative and mask up. Speed of reaction is vital if you are to have any chance. The sequence of actions known as the Immediate Action Drill must be automatic.

The Warsaw Pact has a massive arsenal of chemical weapons. It is unrealistic to imagine that these weapons will not be used in any future large-scale conflict involving NATO. You must be prepared to survive poison gas attack and fight on in a contaminated battlefield.

The chemical survival syllabus is a complete guide to the drills that must become automatic if you are to succeed.

Chemical agent routes of entry into the body

Ingestion
Persistent agents can get into food and water supplies and be absorbed into the bloodstream or contact-damage the stomach. Keep all equipment and food under cover and sealed in plastic once a chemical threat is declared to exist. After an attack, if you are not sure about a food source eat only tinned food that has been under cover.

Inhalation
This is the most usual route. Most agents are more damaging if breathed in rather than absorbed through the skin or eyes.

Inoculation
Biological agents can be carried and injected into you by an insect carrier such as a mosquito, and chemical weapons can be propelled into you by fragments of binary shells. (Those with a high explosive and chemical mix filling).

Absorption
Most chemical agents can be absorbed by the skin, and are especially rapid in contact with lung tissue.

The Chemical Safety rule

Once you are deployed in an operational area where a chemical threat is known to exist, you must have no doubts when to assume you are under chemical attack. The Chemical Safety rule has been devised to cover all the possible situations which could mean an attack. You must learn and understand it.

There is a risk of chemical attack if:
1 You experience a bombardment of any kind.
2 You sight hostile or unknown low-flying aircraft.
3 You see suspicious mist, smoke, droplets or splashes.
4 You smell anything unusual.
5 You notice symptoms in yourself or others of chemical agent poisoning. These are:
- Dimness of vision
- Irritation of the eyes
- A sudden headache
- Tightness of the chest
- Running nose
- Intense salivation, i.e. excess saliva in the mouth
6 You hear the alarm

You must then assume it is a chemical attack and carry out the Immediate Action Drill.

1 On sensing or suspecting the attack, drop down with your back to the wind, close your eyes and stop breathing. Remove your helmet and glasses if you wear them and pull down your hood.

2 Put your chin into the respirator and pull it on. Do not pull it down over your face as liquid contamination on your head will end up inside the respirator. Resist the temptation to take an extra breath: it could be your last.

Delivering chemical agents

A chemical agent can arrive in your location in a variety of ways:

1. Artillery, either shells or mortar bombs or multiple-barrelled rocket launchers.

2. From the air either by bombs, bomblets, sprays or drones which can use any of the preceding methods.

3. Guided or free-flight missiles, as used in the Iran/Iraq war.

4. Chemical mines or grenades.

5. Gas generators.

6. Infantry weapons such as a Very pistol or a rifle grenade.

3 Blow out hard and shout 'GAS, GAS, GAS.' You must do this within nine seconds. Make sure the strap is central on the back of your head and that no hair has fouled the seal of the respirator on the face.

4 Put your hood up and check the seal of the hood round the respirator. If there is cover near at hand, get under cover. Decontaminate your hands quickly but thoroughly with DKP 1 and put on your gloves inner and outer.

5 Check that the hood fits tightly around the face piece. The chin strap goes behind the canister; the gloves go over the cuffs; the haversack must be closed and detector paper must be attached to your body and your kit.

Military uses of chemical agents

While chemical agents have not proved to be a battle- or war-winning weapon in the past, with modern weapons and a massive capability the Soviets' chemical arsenal would certainly provide a significant advantage. Chemical weapons can be used for the following purposes:

1 To inflict mass casualties on an enemy by achieving surprise or by using an agent that is capable of overcoming his defensive equipment.
2 To effectively suppress an enemy position without physically damaging it.
3 To harass an enemy by forcing him to operate in a contaminated environment.
4 To disrupt the logistic back-up and industrial support of an enemy.
5 To delay reinforcement of an area or movement or reserves by forcing them to detour round contaminated areas or forcing them to use protective equipment.

6 To canalise the enemy's movement into killing areas or set up the enemy for a tactical nuclear strike.
7 To make the use of any area extremely hazardous and any task to be carried out in that area more difficult.
8 To create an obstacle or simply improve already-existing ones.
9 To deny the use of abandoned facilities to the enemy by contamination.

Physical forms of chemical agents

When they have been delivered by the above methods they can appear on the target in the following forms:

1 Liquid, either droplets or sprays.
2 Aerosol , a very fine spray made up of liquid droplets or solid powder but so fine that it is invisible to the eye.
3 Vapour, from an evaporating liquid agent.

6 Check your detector paper, which will show blue spots for a liquid agent attack. Get under cover and carry out immediate decontamination as soon as the liquid has stopped falling.

RESPIRATOR AND CANISTER-CHANGING DRILL

HOW TO CHANGE A CANISTER

The Germans did not employ their extensive range of poison gases during World War II only because they believed the Allies had even more deadly chemical weapons of their own. Today, NATO has a very limited arsenal of chemical weapons. The best defence against potential Soviet chemical attack is first class protective equipment and a high standard of training. British Army equipment is good by world standards, so make sure your drills are correct.

The S6 respirator

The S6 respirator and canister will filter out all known chemical and biological agents, and will also prevent you inhaling radioactive dust particles. It will protect the facial skin, eyes, nose, throat and lungs. The respirator is available in three sizes with left-handed models (with the canister on the right) for left-handed shots. You are issued with two canisters initially and more will be issued as the battle continues. It is vital that you know when to change canisters, and you must be able to do so safely.

1 Take cover if possible and check the position of the spare canister in your haversack. Place your right hand around the outlet valve and place your left on the canister. Close your eyes and hold your breath.

ADJUSTING THE RESPIRATOR

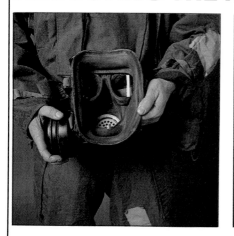

The respirator will only protect you if it functions correctly. Make sure that you get the right size for your face and shave at least once every 48 hours. Short hair will reduce the chances of breaking the seal with hair across your forehead.

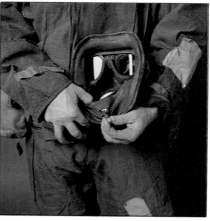

The face piece has a rubber bladder that must be adjusted for atmospheric pressure to ensure an effective seal. Fold out the small valve as shown and unscrew it for a few seconds, then tighten it up. This will equalise the air pressure.

The respirator can be adjusted by altering the tensioning straps on the back of the respirator. The head piece should be in the centre of the back of the head as shown and the facepiece should be firmly held against the face.

SEVEN OCCASIONS WHEN YOU MUST CHANGE YOUR CANISTER

You must know under what circumstances you must change canisters. Learn them by heart: they are vital to your survival. Change your canister:

1 If you suddenly start to feel the effects of a chemical agent or smell something unusual while wearing an otherwise correctly fitting and functioning respirator.
2 If it becomes hard to breathe in or out.
3 After the canister has been completely immersed in water, e.g. while crossing a river.

4 If the canister is particularly badly damaged or dented, especially at the seams.
5 After 120 hours in a chemical environment, except if you are in an armoured fighting vehicle which uses a forced airflow system, where the canister will only last for 40 hours.
6 When the canister's shelf-life has expired (seven years from the date of manufacture stamped on the canister).
7 When you are ordered to change canisters by your local commander.

Levels of protection

Surprise is what chemical warfare is all about. Consequently, many chemical agents cannot be sensed or easily detected. In some cases a droplet, absorbed through the skin and which you can't even feel, is enough to kill you. Protection is therefore based on:

1 Taking the necessary precautions before an attack.
2 Masking up on the suspicion of an attack.
3 Removing any persistent agent that presents a residual hazard as soon as possible.

THREAT LEVELS AND ALARM STATES

THREAT	STATE	PROTECTION
No indication of Offensive use in the immediate future	LOW	All pers carry their protective equipt or have it readily available.
Chemical weapons have been used and/or strong indication of use in immediate future	MED	Suits worn, gloves, overboots, respirators carried or immediately available. Collective protection tested Overhead protection. Defence plan implemented
Chemical attack is imminent	HIGH	Full protection less respirator when outside. Facelet. Collective protection working
Attack on posn or warning of arrival of agents	BLACK	Full protection or in collective protection

2 Keep your eyes closed and do not breathe as you unscrew the old canister and discard it. Keep your right hand in position around the valve with thumb and open fingers ready to locate the new canister.

3 Locate the new canister and screw it up tightly. Then blow out hard to clear your mask of any vapour. You can then open your eyes. Make sure you then dent the old canister so it cannot be mistakenly reused.

4 Thoroughly decontaminate your gloves with DKP 1. This is a pad filled with Fuller's Earth which absorbs liquid chemical agents. The decontamination technique will be covered later.

5 Decontaminate the outside of the respirator paying special attention to the outside of the canister and the face piece. Make sure the respirator haversack is closed and lastly report the canister change to your section commander.

Racing to War with the Warrior

Fast, heavily armed and superbly agile, the British Army's new Warrior mechanised combat vehicle will take you into battle safely, at speed, and in style. But more than the vehicle is new — it represents a new philosophy for combat infantry. The Warrior replaces the FV 432 APC that has served the Army

Above: Leaping into action from a Warrior on Salisbury Plain. The mechanised battalions receiving Warrior will now be designated 'Armoured Infantry' and will fight in a very different way from the old days of the FV 432.

Left: Warrior is the fastest beast on tracks in NATO, capable of astonishing acceleration and fearsome speed cross-country. Victory often goes to the side that gets there 'fastest with the mostest', and Warrior has both the speed and the firepower.

since the early 1960s and followed the successful design pioneered by the US M113 APC. Armoured infantry philosophy at the time demanded a vehicle that could get a section of infantry from A to B on the battlefield in comparative safety. In other words it was an armoured taxi designed to deliver you somewhere short of your objective. Then, you would debus and assault on foot. The FV 432 was not designed to fight from.

Pace and punch

British thinking has, over the years, changed considerably. The result is the MCV (Mechanized Combat Vehicle) 80 or, as it has now been christened by the British Army, the War-

rior. This vehicle, as its name implies, is essentially a *fighting* vehicle. It has the power and mobility to keep up with the Challenger tank and is armed with a 30-mm RARDEN cannon and a Hughes Chain Gun, although it does not have firing ports. The section will still have to dismount short of the objective and continue on foot.

However, Warrior will provide powerful covering fire when you go into the assault. And in defence, your

Overrunning the enemy position under cover of smoke, the section advances by fire and manoeuvre with the Warrior taking out enemy trenches. If the section concentrates on enemy anti-tank rocket men, Warrior's Chain Gun and cannon will do the rest.

Warrior can be dug in, hull-down, behind your position so that it can add its weight of fire to the section's defence.

Go anywhere

Warrior weighs 25.4 tonnes, very nearly twice the weight of the old FV 432. It is also longer, wider and higher than 432. But it is in the performance that you will notice the difference. Whereas the old 432 used to lumber along at a theoretical top speed of 32.5 mph (actually it was nearer

Below: Fighting in support of its seven-man infantry section, Warrior can use its RARDEN 30-mm cannon against enemy defensive positions. The round will penetrate the top cover of a typical battle trench and explode inside.

25 mph because the vehicles were getting so old), Warrior's top road speed is over 50 mph. But its agility, mobility and acceleration are truly impressive: it can reach 30 mph in 18 seconds, which for 25 tonnes is not bad.

The combination of aluminium alloy armour, a powerful engine and a remarkable suspension system means that you can move impressively fast between cover on the battlefield. This means that you and the rest of your section will be exposed to enemy fire for shorter periods of time.

This is terribly important. Modern anti-tank guided missiles fly quite fast out to their maximum range (MILAN, for instance, takes 13 seconds to reach 2000 metres). Thus, if you are at about 1500 metres from a Soviet ATGW system, you probably have about 10 seconds (including acquisition time) to motor from one bit of cover to the next. In Warrior, depending on the terrain, that might be possible. In 432 it almost certainly would not.

Inside the Warrior

And in Warrior you can shoot back. It is armed with a 30-mm RARDEN cannon, which is capable of firing APDS (Armour Piercing Discarding Sabot) and HE rounds out to 2000 metres. Two hundred and twenty-five rounds are carried inside the turret. The 7.62-mm Hughes Chain Gun, mounted co-axially in the turret, can shoot out to 1100 metres.

Answer back

Despite this considerable fire-power, you should not use Warrior as a tank. It has nothing like the same sort of protection as Challenger – no APC or MCV has. The RARDEN is designed to take out enemy APCs, and the Hughes Chain Gun is designed to support you when you are dis-mounted from the vehicle. If the gun-ner in a Warrior was foolish enough to take on a tank, there is no doubt who would come off worst.

The vehicle does have some anti-tank capability; LAW 80s are carried in the troop compartment and can be fired from the roof hatches (although normally the section will be dis-mounted when firing them). They can even be fired from the turret by the commander or gunner. Firing from the vehicle could be a useful tactic in close country or built-up areas.

Warrior is also equipped with multi-barrel smoke dischargers, which are mounted either side of the turret and fire forwards. They dis-charge a pattern of smoke grenades to create an instant smoke screen be-tween you and the enemy. This is often useful if you are under fire and need to extricate yourself quickly. The turret is equipped with a Raven ×8 day sight and fully integrated image intensifier (II) night sight, so that the vehicle can operate 24 hours a day.

Warrior is designed to carry a total of 10 men, including a vehicle com-mander and driver. Because Warrior is designed to support the section

Warrior will change British mechanized infantry out of all recognition. Now called Armoured Infantry, battalions will need increased manpower with an additional junior NCO in every Warrior. He will command the vehicle when the section commander and 2-i-c dismount with the infantry fire teams.

Commander

7.62-mm Chain Gun
Electrically driven, the Chain Gun ejects a hail of cases out of the turret and is a great improvement over most turret-mounted machine-guns because it does not fill the turret with fumes.

RARDEN 30-mm cannon

Smoke rocket dischargers

Driver
Driving the Warrior is enormous fun; its speed and acceleration are a delight. On German autobahns and British motorways, Warriors have been found exceeding the speed limit. Full marks to the vehicle, but not to the drivers concerned!

Aluminium hull armour
This is used instead of steel to reduce the weight of the vehicle.

Warrior could have been made as low as the Soviet BMP series, but the decision was made to increase the headroom in the troop compartment. This makes life much more comfortable for the men in the back.

when it dismounts, the vehicle com-mander remains with the vehicle acquiring targets and loading the RARDEN cannon when the section dismounts. Two fire teams, one of four men and one of three, will debus, both armed with an LSW. The vehicle itself will act as a third fireteam. The section commander will lead one team, the section second-in-command will command the other, and an additional JNCO will command the vehicle.

The crew compartment is inevit-ably cramped but has been carefully designed to give you reasonable head-room. The latest suspension system is

Racing to War with the Warrior

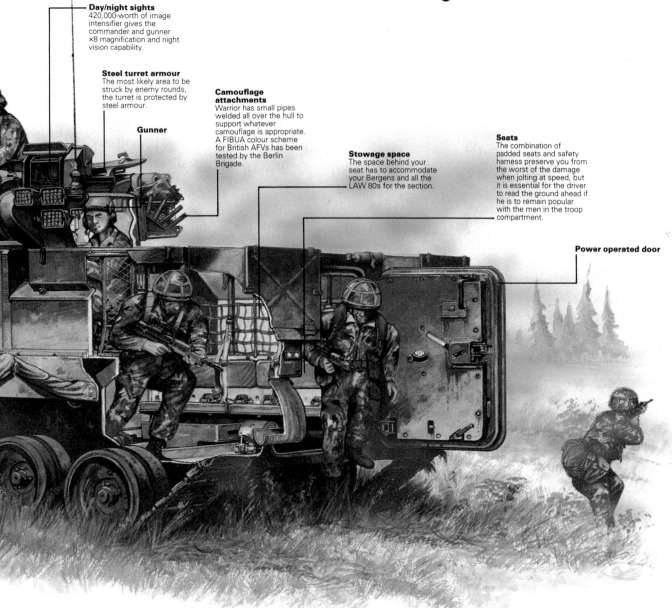

Day/night sights
420,000-worth of image intensifier gives the commander and gunner ×8 magnification and night vision capability.

Steel turret armour
The most likely area to be struck by enemy rounds, the turret is protected by steel armour.

Gunner

Camouflage attachments
Warrior has small pipes welded all over the hull to support whatever camouflage is appropriate. A FIBUA colour scheme for British AFVs has been tested by the Berlin Brigade.

Stowage space
The space behind your seat has to accommodate your Bergens and all the LAW 80s for the section.

Seats
The combination of padded seats and safety harness preserve you from the worst of the damage when jolting at speed, but it is essential for the driver to read the ground ahead if he is to remain popular with the men in the troop compartment.

Power operated door

that it can easily be adapted for any number of roles. Thirteen variants are planned, including two versions of an APC, a command vehicle, a recovery vehicle, a combat repair vehicle, mor-

Warrior is specifically designed to stay in action in NBC conditions. If you have to stay masked up, your combat efficiency is quickly reduced. Warrior's filtration system allows you to remove your respirator while inside, helping to keep you fit for action.

excellent but you still need the individual harness during high-speed cross-country driving. There is the usual large container for boiling hot water electrically, which means you can still indulge in the all-important "brews" to keep body and soul together! But, even more important, the vehicle is fitted with a highly efficient air filtration system.

The Warrior family

Most new armoured vehicles spawn a whole range of variants and become, in time, a "family" of vehicles. Warrior has been designed so

tar, ATGW, recce and anti-aircraft vehicles, rocket launcher and load carrying vehicles, and even a 30-tonne light battle tank mounting a 105-mm gun. Some of these variants exist and will be brought into service with the British Army; others remain on the drawing board. The Warrior project is an exciting one, with a great future. The main job of Warrior, though, is to carry the infantryman

The speed and firepower of Warrior will allow Armoured Infantry to operate at a cracking pace. A Warrior can beast its way from one end of Salisbury Plain to the other in little more than an hour.

Battlefield Evaluation: comparing

Warrior

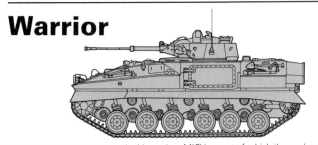

Warrior can only be compared with modern MICVs, most of which themselves have been the subject of previous features. The expense of building your own MICV is so great that only a few countries have produced their own. As the fastest NATO MICV and probably the most capable, it is to be hoped that Warrior will do well in the export market.

Specification:
Crew: 3+7
Combat weight: 24.5 tonnes
Road speed: 120 km/h +
Power to weight ratio: 22.45 hp/tonne
Length: 6.34 m
Height: 2.7 m overall
Armament: 1x30-mm RARDEN cannon; 1x7.62-mm Chain Gun

Assessment
Firepower   ★★★★
Protection   ★★★
Age   ★
Worldwide users   ★

With Warrior, the British Infantry has at last received a first-class fighting vehicle.

M2 Bradley

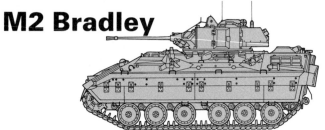

Warrior is armoured against 14.5-mm machine-guns carried by Soviet recce vehicles like the BRDM, but the US Army is now planning to armour the Bradley against the 30-mm cannon fitted to BMP-2. This will substantially increase weight, decrease battlefield mobility and probably remove amphibious capability. The Bradley's greater firepower reflects the American preference for weight of suppressive fire.

Specification:
Crew: 3+7
Combat weight: 22.5 tonnes (original M2)
Road speed: 66 km/h
Power to weight ratio: 20 hp/tonne
Length: 6.45 m
Height: 2.97 m
Armament: 25-mm cannon; 7.62-mm machine-gun; 5.56-mm rifles from firing ports; TOW ATGMs

Assessment
Firepower   ★★★★★
Protection   ★★★
Age   ★
Worldwide users   ★

In the USA the debate over Bradley's capabilities continues to rage.

BMP-1

The original BMP is rendered obsolete by Warrior. It has no headroom, so the combat value of the infantry section is rapidly degraded. Firing from within the vehicle fills it with fumes. Its armour protection is weaker and it burns well. The 73-mm smoothbore gun is inaccurate over 800 metres, and stopping to fire 'Sagger' in the middle of a mobile battle is a recipe for disaster.

Specification:
Crew: 3+8
Combat weight: 13.5 tonnes
Road speed: 80 km/h
Power to weight ratio: 22 hp/tonne
Length: 6.74 m
Height: 2.15 m
Armament: 1x73-mm smoothbore gun; 'Sagger' ATGM; 1x7.62-mm machine-gun

Assessment
Firepower   ★★
Protection   ★★★
Age   ★★★★
Wordwide users   ★★★★

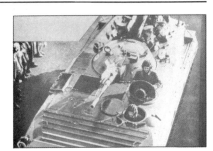

The BMP-1 is now looking very outclassed with its weak armament and reputation for brewing up.

into battle and support him when he gets there. This is where you come in. The British infantryman now has a fighter vehicle which is probably better than the US Bradley or the German Marder. It is certainly superior to any Soviet equivalents. Soldiering in a mechanised infantry battalion in Germany has suddenly taken on a new lease of life – it's called soldiering in the fast lane!

Bouncing about in the back of a Warrior can be an exciting experience to say the least, but you can take comfort from the knowledge that your Soviet counterpart is having an even rougher time in a cramped and slower vehicle.

the Warrior with its rivals

BMP-2

With an effective 30-mm cannon and 'Spandrel' ATGM, the BMP-2 is a dangerous opponent for Warrior. Fully amphibious and with NBC system, its most significant disadvantage is the low troop compartment, which squashes the riflemen together. A high-speed cross-country drive in the back of any MICV will leave you sick and exhausted, but it is worse in a BMP. Firing ports for the section's rifles simply fill the troop compartment with fumes and empty cases.

Specification:
Crew: 3+7
Combat weight: 14.6 tonnes
Road speed: 65 km/h (estimate)
Power to weight ratio: unknown
Length: 6.71 m
Height: 2 m
Armament: 1x30-mm cannon: 1x'Spandrel' ATGM; 1x7.62-mm machine-gun

Assessment
Firepower   ★★★★
Protection   ★★★
Age   ★
Worldwide users   ★

The BMP-2 retains the typical low silhouette of a Soviet AFV.

BMD

If the Soviet airborne forces ever do drop in on BAOR, Warriors will race to take on the light, airportable BMD. The BMD is designed to give the Soviet paras extra mobility and the ability to bounce inferior forces or units taken by surprise. The limitations of the airmobile design give it huge disadvantages as an MICV, but it is a lot better than nothing.

Specification:
Crew: 7
Combat weight: 6.7 tonnes
Road speed: 70 km/h
Power to weight ratio: 35 hp/tonne
Length: 5.4 m
Height: 1.97 m
Armament: 1x73-mm gun; 3x7.62-mm machine-guns; 'Sagger' or 'Spigot' ATGM

Assessment
Firepower   ★★★
Protection   ★
Age   ★★★
Worldwide users   ★

The BMD is another likely opponent for British Armoured Infantry.

AMX-10

Like Warrior, the AMX-10 has an aluminium alloy hull to save weight and like the Marder, its 20-mm cannon in the Toucan II turret is mounted externally. Twin ammunition feed allows the gunner to switch quickly between HE and AP rounds. To meet the increasing speeds of the modern battlefield, the 280-hp engine may be replaced by a 350-hp model in the near future.

Specification:
Crew: 3+8
Combat weight: 14.5 tonnes
Road speed: 65 km/h
Power to weight ratio: 20 hp/tonne
Length: 5.78 m
Height: 2.57 m
Armament: 1x20-mm cannon; 1x7.62-mm machine-gun

Assessment
Firepower   ★★
Protection   ★★★
Age   ★★★★
Worldwide users   ★★

Like the Soviet MICVs, the AMX-10 is designed as a lightweight vehicle with amphibious capability in mind.

Simonov's Cold War Carbine

Main Force Viet Cong overrun a South Vietnamese position in 1965. The soldier on the left carries an SKS with the bayonet extended. The first Soviet rifle to fire their new intermediate power 7.62mm cartridge, the SKS was quickly replaced by the AK-47 but millions were made and were supplied to communist allies all over the world.

When the Kalashnikov assault rifles were adopted by the Soviet army, they replaced a conventional self-loading rifle chambered for the same cartridge. The SKS had already been copied by North Korea, Yugoslavia and China and it continues to turn up in the hands of armies and guerrilla movements all over Africa and Asia.

Sergei Simonov had a long apprenticeship in the weapons business. Born in 1894, by 1917 he was working with Fedorov on his automatic rifle. After the Revolution, Simonov

studied engineering and in 1926 was Inspector at Tula Arsenal. In the following year he was in the design department, once again working under Fedorov. In the early 1930s he designed the AVS automatic rifle, which was taken into Soviet service in 1936; chambered for the 7.62×54R cartridge, it had selective fire capability and was a bit of a handful to fire. It was never very popular and never made in any quantity.

After this he designed the 14.5-mm PTRS self-loading anti-tank rifle, which was effective against smaller

Members of a Rhodesian Light Infantry patrol inspect weapons captured after ambushing a ZIPRA unit. Note the Yugoslavian SKS, the M59/66 A1, distinguished by the muzzle brake/grenade launcher. The other weapons include a Russian PKM light machine gun and two Chinese 60mm mortars.

Load and unload procedure

1 Apply the safety catch and rack back the cocking handle. If the magazine is empty the magazine follower will engage the hold open device and hold the bolt open.

2 Take a 10 round charger and insert it into the charger guide on the top of the bolt carrier. Wrap your thumb round one side of the clip and support the other side with your fingers. Push the cartridges down into the magazine with constant pressure.

3 Make sure the top round is correctly seated in the top of the magazine and pull the stripper clip out of the guide. Pull back slightly on the bolt and the mainspring will drive the bolt forward, chambering the first round ready to fire.

4 To unload the weapon pull back on the magazine catch and the rounds in the magazine will drop out. Then pull back on the bolt to eject the round in the chamber.

armoured vehicles, and finally, in about 1945-6, he amalgamated the best features of the PTRS and the SVS and produced the SKS – the Samozaryadnyi Karabin Simonova.

The SKS was the first Soviet weapon to be chambered for the 7.62×39-mm M43 cartridge. There has always been some doubt as to how much of this cartridge is native Russian and how much was inspired by the German 7.92 *Kurz* assault rifle round; the Soviets were certainly experimenting with small calibres and short cases in the 1930s, but without coming to any firm conclusions, and it seems likely that once the Germans adopted the short cartridge, the Soviets dusted off their pre-war reports and came up with the 7.62×39 round. In any event, it was what Simonov needed to make his rifle work, since the full-power 7.62 round had

given excessive blast and recoil – so much so that a hefty muzzle brake had to be added to the AVS of 1936 to make it tolerable.

Gas operation

The SKS carbine uses a gas operating system, with the gas cylinder above the barrel: a similar arrangement to that used with the Kalashnikov rifle. The bolt system had been first used by Simonov with his PTRS rifle and carried over to the SKS. The bolt is held in a bolt carrier, and interconnecting cams on bolt and carrier are arranged so that as the carrier goes forward to load, the bolt pushes a cartridge into the chamber and its rear end is then forced down by the carrier so as to lock in front of a lug in the receiver. On firing, gas tapped from the barrel enters the gas cylinder and drives a piston backwards; this strikes

Right: Two Mujahideen of the NIFA group proudly display their weapons on the infiltration route from Pakistan. The SKS is a Chinese Type 56 carbine with the cruciform bayonet. SKS rifles are used mainly to arm supply convoys coming over the border rather than in attacks against the Russians and government troops as NIFA has enough Kalashnikovs to go round.

Inside the SKS

The SKS is a conventional gas-piston operated, tilting block locked, semi-automatic rifle. It is no longer in Soviet service except for ceremonial purposes. However, it is still in use in several Asian countries and equips communist backed guerrilla organisations such as SWAPO in Namibia. Large quantities of Chinese SKS Type 56 carbines are being used against the Soviets by the Mujahideen in Afghanistan.

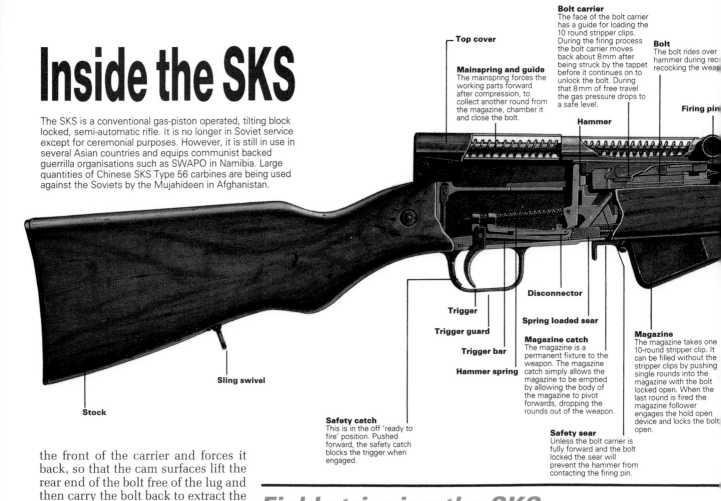

Top cover

Bolt carrier
The face of the bolt carrier has a guide for loading the 10 round stripper clips. During the firing process the bolt carrier moves back about 8mm after being struck by the tappet before it continues on to unlock the bolt. During that 8mm of free travel the gas pressure drops to a safe level.

Bolt
The bolt rides over hammer during rec recocking the weap

Firing pin

Mainspring and guide
The mainspring forces the working parts forward after compression, to collect another round from the magazine, chamber it and close the bolt.

Hammer

Disconnector

Trigger

Spring loaded sear

Trigger guard

Magazine catch
The magazine is a permanent fixture to the weapon. The magazine catch simply allows the magazine to be emptied by allowing the body of the magazine to pivot forwards, dropping the rounds out of the weapon.

Trigger bar

Magazine
The magazine takes one 10-round stripper clip. It can be filled without the stripper clips by pushing single rounds into the magazine with the bolt locked open. When the last round is fired the magazine follower engages the hold open device and locks the bolt open.

Hammer spring

Sling swivel

Stock

Safety catch
This is in the off 'ready to fire' position. Pushed forward, the safety catch blocks the trigger when engaged.

Safety sear
Unless the bolt carrier is fully forward and the bolt locked the sear will prevent the hammer from contacting the firing pin.

the front of the carrier and forces it back, so that the cam surfaces lift the rear end of the bolt free of the lug and then carry the bolt back to extract the spent case, eject it, and then cock the hammer.

The SKS retains the old style of fixed magazine, loaded from a 10-round charger or by adding loose rounds. To empty the magazine quickly, the rear end can be released, allowing the casing to swing down from a front hinge so that the rounds drop out into your waiting hands (or the waiting mud, as the case may be). The stock is also traditional: a long, good-quality wood stock with a separate handguard covering the gas cylinder; but later models often use a form of resin-bonded plywood. The most distinctive feature is the permanently-attached blade bayonet which is hinged beneath the barrel and lies in a slot in the fore-end of the stock. To 'fix' it, pull the handle to the rear to release a spring catch, and swing the bayonet through 180° until it latches on to a lug beneath the foresight. This lug also acts as the front guide for the cleaning rod.

Battle setting

The rear sight is a U-notch on a hinged arm; there is a slider which, when moved, hinges the arm up to give the necessary elevation. A 'battle' setting covers everything out to 300 metres, after which you have to set the range required, in 100 m steps to

Field stripping the SKS

1 All the different types of SKS field-strip in the same way. Pull the magazine catch back to empty the mag of cartridges. Clear the weapon and leave it cocked. Release the bayonet and pivot it down through 90 degrees.

2 Remove the cleaning rod, pulling it out forwards. Next, locate the takedown lever on the right-hand side of the weapon at the base of the top cover. Rotate the lever anti-clockwise 180 degrees and you will then be able to pull the lever out.

6 Slide the bolt out of the recesses which hold it in the carrier. The bolt will usually drop out, so have a careful look at the way it goes together for reassembling.

7 The gas parts are removed by rotating the take-down lever on the rearsight mounting upwards.

Simonov's Cold War Carbine

Cocking handle
The cocking handle is permanently attached to the bolt carrier. After loading with a 10 round clip and removing the stripper clip, the first round is chambered by pulling back on the cocking handle and releasing.

Chamber

Rear sight
This is a conventional ramp type sight as on the AK-47 which is adjustable in 100m settings. The 'v' notch and post give a clear sight picture.

Tappet
The tappet acts as a connecting rod between the gas piston and the face of the bolt carrier.

Gas piston
The gas piston is forced back against spring pressure by the gas tapped off from the barrel and forces the bolt carrier back via a tappet unlocking the action. After the initial blow from the piston the working parts move back, extracting and ejecting the empty case and recocking the hammer.

Gas port
When the weapon fires, expanding gases behind the bullet are vented through this hole to act against the piston rod in the gas tube.

Barrel
The barrel is longer than that of the AK-47 and the weapon is generally more accurate than the Kalashnikov designs.

Muzzle
The bayonet ring fits over the muzzle by pulling the bayonet grip sleeve out against spring pressure and slotting it over the muzzle to lock it in place.

Foresight
This is a conventional protected post which is adjustable for windage and elevation.

Piston spring
This returns the tappet and piston to its original position after the gas pressure has compressed it during the firing sequence. It is a short stroke action.

Finger groove

Bayonet
Russian SKS rifles have this type of folding knife bayonet that is permanently fixed to the rifle. Later models of the Chinese Type 56 carbine have folding spike type bayonets.

Cleaning rod
Cleaning rods are a lot more effective for cleaning the barrel than the pull through. The rod has to be removed prior to field stripping and is locked in place by the bayonet that has to be pivoted downwards to release it.

7.62mm×39 Russian
This round is the intermediate round used in the AK-47, AKM, and RPK etc. It is not as powerful or accurate as the 7.62mm NATO but is effective over normal battlefield engagement ranges.

The Yugoslavian M59/66A1 rifle has a permanently attached spigot-type grenade launcher. Launching the grenade involves folding up the grenade sight and cutting off the gas to the gas piston by pressing in the cut-off valve.

3 The lever releases the top cover, which can then be lifted off to reveal the recoil spring and guide and the bolt and bolt carrier.

4 Push in on the back of the recoil spring and lift it out of the retaining catch to remove backwards from the weapon.

5 Slide both the bolt and bolt carrier back until you can lift them out of the receiver when the carrier corresponds to the cut-outs in the receiver. When you put the working parts back in, remember to press the magazine floor plate in to release the hold-open device.

8 The gas tube and piston will then lift up and to the rear. The piston and the tube and the area of the vent from the barrel tend to be fouled with carbon after firing and will need careful cleaning.

9 The gas piston will simply drop out of the gas tube forwards.

10 The SKS field-stripped with a few 10-round chargers of 7.62×39. Reassemble the weapon in reverse order. Although very dated, it is a solid weapon that, like the AK, handles well and will put up with a lot of abuse and misuse.

1000 m maximum. The foresight is a hooded post which can be screwed up and down with the issued combination tool to alter the point of impact when zeroing the rifle.

Comfortable weapon

The SKS weighs over 4 kg which, strangely, is considerably less than the original AK-47 but about the same as the AKM. But it feels more like a rifle than the AKs do, and is comfort-

A Rhodesian Fire Force team take a break after a successful contact during which these two Chinese Type 56 carbines were captured. These weapons were excellent souvenirs as they could be swopped for goodies from the REMFS back at base.

Battlefield Evaluation: comparing

SKS 7.62-mm carbine

The SKS was the first Soviet weapon developed to fire their new 'intermediate' 7.62-mm cartridge. A solid, if uninspired design, the SKS was churned out in vast numbers during the 1950s and was supplied to most communist forces. Replaced by the Kalashnikov series of assault rifles, it spread into guerrilla hands and was a popular weapon with the Viet Cong until they received enough AK-47s.

Specification:
Cartridge: 7.63 mm×39
Weight: 3.85 kg empty
Length: 1021 mm
Cyclic rate of fire: single shot
Magazine: 10-round box

Assessment
Reliability   ★★★
Accuracy   ★★
Age   ★★★★★
Worldwide users   ★★

Although more of a rifleman's weapon than the later AKs the SKS is a less effective battlefield weapon.

Fusil Automatique Modèle 49

Also known as the 'SAFN', 'ABL' or 'Saive', this gas-operated self-loading rifle was designed before World War II by D.J. Saive in the FN works in Belgium. He fled to England during the war and continued to develop the gun, offering it to the British Army, who rejected it. Back in Belgium after the war it was placed in production and did very well. Built to a high standard, it was expensive to manufacture but proved popular, partly because it was available in many calibres.

Specification:
Cartridge: 7 mm, 7.65 mm, 7.92 mm or .30 cal
Weight: 4.31 kg
Length: 1116 mm
Cyclic rate of fire: single shot
Magazine: 10-round box

Assessment
Reliability   ★★★
Accuracy   ★★★
Age   ★★★★★
Worldwide users   ★

FN produced this weapon to very high standards and in various calibres.

M14

The US Army already had a self-loading rifle in service before World War II, the M1 Garand. The M14 was simply a development of the Garand with a box magazine instead of the clip, so it is half a generation ahead of the SKS. A handful on full auto but an excellent weapon firing single shots, the M14 is certainly a better weapon than the SKS.

Specification:
Cartridge: 7.62 mm×51
Weight: 5.1 kg
Length: 1120 mm
Cyclic rate of fire: 700 rounds per minute
Magazine: 20-round box

Assessment
Reliability   ★★★
Accuracy   ★★★
Age   ★★★★
Worldwide users   ★

The M14 was one of the most accurate military self loaders ever produced, and was in an entirely different league to the SKS.

able to shoot, being well-matched to the cartridge. Although it was superseded in the Soviet service by the Kalashnikovs (because they were cheaper and easier to make), the SKS is still carried for ceremonial purposes. It has, of course, been exported in great quantities to wherever Soviet influence has been making itself felt over the past 30-odd years, so you are likely to run into the SKS anywhere in the world.

Favoured guerrilla weapons: the SKS handles and shoots very well and weighs about the same as the AKM above it, and is only marginally bigger than the PPsh sub machine gun below. But it was expensive to manufacture and lacked the AK's firepower for close quarter battle.

the SKS with its rivals

AK53

The Swiss company SIG produced several self-loading rifles during World War II but the post-war AK53 was one of the most unusual rifle designs in recent history. The barrel moved forward while the bolt remained stationary: this reduced the length but led to a host of new problems, e.g. low cyclic rate of fire and the potential risk of cook-off since it fired from a closed breach. It never sold and simply proves that even the better arms manufacturers sometimes produce a turkey.

Specification:
Cartridge: 7.5mm
Weight: 4.9kg empty
Length: 1000mm
Cyclic rate of fire: 300 rounds per minute
Magazine: 30-round box

Assessment
Reliability	**
Accuracy	**
Age	*****
Worldwide users	—

The AK 53 was a unique and well manufactured complete failure.

MAS 49/56

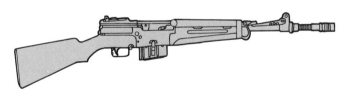

The French were also quick off the mark with a self-loader, introducing this tough and highly reliable weapon in 1949. It served the French army very well in Indo-China and Algeria and is a better weapon than the SKS in most respects. The only drawback for non-French forces, is the use of the French 7.5-mm cartridge, but some have been produced in 7.62-mm NATO.

Specification:
Cartridge: 7.5mm×54
Weight: 4.5kg
Length: 1010mm
Cyclic rate of fire: single shot
Magazine: 10-round box

Assessment
Reliability	***
Accuracy	***
Age	*****
Worldwide users	**

The MAS 49 used by the French in Vietnam was later to be used alongside the SKS by the VC.

vz 52

The vz 52 was a self-loading rifle developed in Czechoslovakia in the brief interlude between German and Soviet occupation. Its operation was largely cribbed from the MKb42(W), a Walther-designed wartime German assault rifle, and the trigger was copied from the M1 Garand. Chambered for the Czech 7.62-mm round, some were modified to fire 7.62-mm×39 after the Czech forces were incorporated into the Warsaw Pact. The Czech army dropped the vz 52 like a brick as soon as supplies of the vz 58 assault rifle began to arrive.

Specification:
Cartridge: 7.62mm vz 52
Weight: 4.6kg
Length: 1003mm
Cyclic rate of fire: single shot
Magazine: 10-round box

Assessment
Reliability	***
Accuracy	***
Age	*****
Worldwide users	—

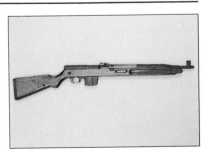

The odd calibre really limited the appeal of this rifle, although a few were made in 7.62mm×39.

On Externals with the Eland

You will encounter the French Panhard AML series of armoured cars all over the world. Used by over 35 different armies, it is also manufactured under licence in South Africa and has seen a great deal of action in Namibia and Angola. The vehicle was designed after the French

An Eland Mk 7, the current production model, fitted with the 90-mm gun, which will fire HEAT rounds accurately out to 1,000 m. Elands have proved to be more than a match for T-34/85 tanks, as South African crews tend to get the first round away faster and more accurately than poorly-trained Angolan crews.

army's experience with British Ferret armoured cars during the Algerian war, the first AMLs entering service with the French army shortly after the abortive coup led by the Foreign Legion paras.

The AML 90 is fitted with a Hispano-Suiza turret. The commander and the gunner both have four periscopes; the latter also has an M37×6 magnification sighting periscope. Doors are situated on both sides of the hull beneath the turret ring. The spare wheel is concealed in the compartment behind the rearward opening left door, and the small area behind the right door provides the crew with its only storage area for personal kit and equipment as well as brew-kit and rations – a perennial problem in all armoured reconnaissance vehicles.

The main armament is a 90-mm D921 Fi gun which can fire HEAT

(high explosive anti-tank), HE, smoke or canister rounds and is aimed with the assistance of a 7.62-mm co-axial machine-gun positioned to its left. A further 7.62-mm (or occasionally a 12.7-mm) anti-aircraft machine-gun may be mounted on the roof. It is not stabilised and therefore ineffective on

The 90-mm gun can fire HE and smoke in addition to the HEAT round. The Eland has also been successful against Cuban-crewed T-54 and T-55 tanks, but with an increase in aid from the Cubans the situation may change as enemy tanks are encountered in larger numbers.

The Eland covers the LS as a Puma comes in with the infantry on operations. Note the high thorn bushes, which are used by the local inhabitants to form kraals for their cattle. The Eland's tyres may be puncture-proof as far as machine-gun fire goes, but the stumps of the thorn bushes have been known to rip them off completely.

The alternative weapon for the Eland is the 60-mm mortar. There is a 20-mm cannon turret which has recently been trialled and is now being retro-fitted to the older models.

the move, but the gun is capable of a rapid rate of fire, can traverse through 360° in 20 seconds and can be elevated from +15° to –8°. Twin SS-11 or ENTAC ATGWs were offered with early models, but were not effective and were withdrawn.

The Lynx-90 turret

Hispano-Suiza has developed an excellent Lynx-90 turret suitable for retro-fitting to a number of French produced armoured cars, including the Panhard AML. Of all-welded steel construction, the turret, with its front armour of 15 mm, is proof against small-arms fire but would offer little protection against the range of ammunition mounted on the majority of modern MICVs (Mechanized Infantry Combat Vehicles.) The commander (seated on the left) and the gunner (to his right) both have single-piece hatch covers and adjustable seats. In com-

This is the blast of the 90-mm night-firing. The Eland can certainly hand out punishment but is not good at taking it, as 15 mm of front armour will only stop 7.62-mm small-arms fire.

mon with French main battle tanks, the commander has a raised rotating cupola for greater all-round observation, which can pintle-mount a 7.62-mm machine-gun for anti-aircraft defence.

In 1983 the much improved Lynx 75/90 turret, capable of mounting the 90-mm Cockerill Mk III gun, the Thompson Brandt breech-loaded mortar and a variety of smaller 75-mm guns, was introduced. Power controlled with manual override, it can turn through 360° in only eight seconds and so can engage enemy forward reconnaissance vehicles before they have the chance to retaliate. Vehicle commanders know that at short ranges such vehicles rarely miss, so the ability to strike the enemy first is a great comfort.

The Eland

In the early 1960s South Africa obtained a licence from Panhard to undertake production of the AML. Since then Sandock-Austal Beperk Limited of Boksburg in the Transvaal, has produced several thousand models, of which 1,600 are currently in service. Designated the Eland, the original design incorporated a 60-mm mortar platform and twin 7.62-mm machine-guns. Since then, numerous improvements have been incorporated as a result of combat experience in Zimbabwe (a few models were exported to the Smith regime prior to Independence) and Namibia. The latest models have a powerful petrol engine specially geared to the hot, dry climates of the bush and a new transmission, all of which can be changed even in field conditions in 40 minutes.

Current production models are armed with a 90-mm gun, 7.62-mm co-axial and 7.62-mm anti-aircraft machine-gun. At the moment well-trained South African crews are prov-

Inside the AML 90

The AML 90, as far as export sales are concerned, is one of the most successful armoured vehicles in history. It is cheap, robust, easy to produce and easy to update with new technology. This combat-proven vehicle is likely to be in service well into the next century.

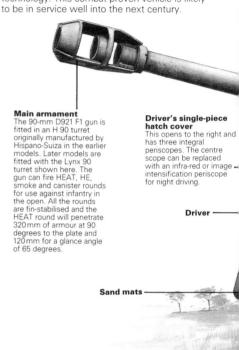

Main armament
The 90-mm D921 F1 gun is fitted in an H 90 turret originally manufactured by Hispano-Suiza in the earlier models. Later models are fitted with the Lynx 90 turret shown here. The gun can fire HEAT, HE, smoke and canister rounds for use against infantry in the open. All the rounds are fin-stabilised and the HEAT round will penetrate 320 mm of armour at 90 degrees to the plate and 120 mm for a glance angle of 65 degrees.

Driver's single-piece hatch cover
This opens to the right and has three integral periscopes. The centre scope can be replaced with an infra-red or image-intensification periscope for night driving.

Driver

Sand mats

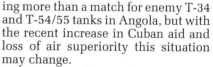

All-welded steel hull
This is divided into three compartments: the driver's compartment, a fighting compartment in the centre, and the engine compartment at the rear.

ing more than a match for enemy T-34 and T-54/55 tanks in Angola, but with the recent increase in Cuban aid and loss of air superiority this situation may change.

Easy to produce and 95 per cent domestic, the Eland is an excellent weapon system for embargo-hit South Africa. A new two-man turret capable of mounting a 20-mm cannon and co-axial 7.62-mm machine-gun has recently been developed and is now being retro-fitted to a few existing chassis. The Eland has given magnificent service to South Africa for nearly three decades, and it will continue to form a crucial part of the SADF's equipment for many years to come.

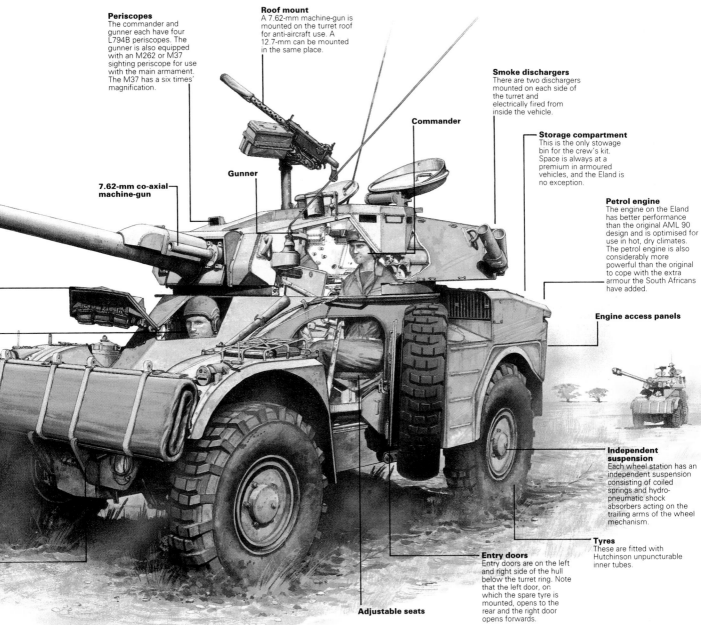

Periscopes
The commander and gunner each have four L794B periscopes. The gunner is also equipped with an M262 or M37 sighting periscope for use with the main armament. The M37 has a six times' magnification.

Roof mount
A 7.62-mm machine-gun is mounted on the turret roof for anti-aircraft use. A 12.7-mm can be mounted in the same place.

Commander

Smoke dischargers
There are two dischargers mounted on each side of the turret and electrically fired from inside the vehicle.

Storage compartment
This is the only stowage bin for the crew's kit. Space is always at a premium in armoured vehicles, and the Eland is no exception.

Gunner

7.62-mm co-axial machine-gun

Petrol engine
The engine on the Eland has better performance than the original AML 90 design and is optimised for use in hot, dry climates. The petrol engine is also considerably more powerful than the original to cope with the extra armour the South Africans have added.

Engine access panels

Independent suspension
Each wheel station has an independent suspension consisting of coiled springs and hydro-pneumatic shock absorbers acting on the trailing arms of the wheel mechanism.

Tyres
These are fitted with Hutchinson unpuncturable inner tubes.

Entry doors
Entry doors are on the left and right side of the hull below the turret ring. Note that the left door, on which the spare tyre is mounted, opens to the rear and the right door opens forwards.

Adjustable seats

Variants

In the best traditions of French design, the AML is capable of accepting several different turrets and weapon systems, of which the most popular is based on the Hispano-Suiza HE-60 series. Two initial models, the H60-7 and H60-12, are each equipped with a Thompson Brandt 60-mm mortar supported by twin 7.62-mm machine-guns and a 12.7-mm heavy machine-gun respec-

Eland crews who are providing flank protection for the convoy on the road clean the main armament prior to moving out. The Eland has good cross-country performance and the new petrol engine gives an excellent power-to-weight ratio.

This South African armoured patrol is 55 miles inside Angola, withdrawing after a successful raid on SWAPO bases in the country. Note the turrets traversed to cover the bush on the sides of the road. Vehicles are fairly close together, but the air threat has significantly increased since 1983 when this raid took place.

tively. Despite its comparatively small size, the two-man all-welded cast turret can hold 43 rounds of mortar ammunition and either 3,800 rounds of 7.62-mm or 1,300 rounds of 12.7-mm. It is fully traversable in 25 seconds and capable of a motor traverse of −15° to +80°, making it a highly effective Third World weapon system. A later variant, the Serval 60/20, has recently entered service and is already proving an export success. It can accept the HB 60 60-mm mortar capable of a direct fire range of 1,000 metres supported by a 20-mm cannon mounted externally at the rear of the turret.

A number of smaller, less complex

Battlefield Evaluation: comparing

AML 90

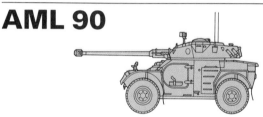

South Africa obtained a licence from Panhard to build the AML 90 in the early 1960s and, as the Eland, it has proved a highly successful combat vehicle. The Eland Mk 1 carried a 60-mm mortar and twin 7.62-mm machine-guns, making it a useful fire support vehicle. Various improved models followed and the ultimate Mk 7 Eland incorporated many changes as a result of combat experience: more armour, new transmission and suspension, new turret and a petrol engine which could be changed in under an hour.

Specification:
Crew: 3
Combat weight: 5.5 tonnes
Road speed: 90 km/h
Power to weight ratio: 16.36 hp/tonne
Length: 3.79 m
Height: 2.07 m overall
Armament: 1×90-mm gun; 1×7.62-mm machine-gun

Assessment
Firepower   *****
Protection   **
Age   *****
Worldwide users   ***

The Eland has proved an excellent fire support vehicle for bush war ops.

Panhard VBL

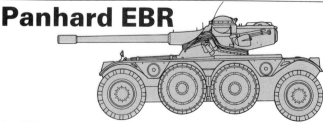

Adopted by the French army in 1985, the VBL (Véhicule Blindé Léger) has two roles: anti-tank and reconnaissance. For the former role it is fitted with MILAN anti-tank missiles and for recce missions carries either a .50-cal or 7.62-mm machine-gun. It is fully amphibious, powered in the water by a propeller in the hull rear. The Michelin tyres are run-flats which allow it to travel 50 km at 30 km/h after a puncture. NBC and/or air conditioning systems are optional.

Specification:
Crew: 2 (recce) 3 (anti-tank)
Combat weight: 3.59 tonnes
Road speed: 100 km/h+
Power to weight ratio: 29.58 hp/tonne
Length: 3.7 m
Height: 1.7 m to hull top
Armament: MILAN or 1×.50-cal or 7.62-mm machine-gun

Assessment
Firepower   *****
Protection   *
Age   *
Worldwide users   *

The VBL would not be ideal for SADF use as it is too small and does not have the range of the Eland.

Panhard EBR

The EBR is a 'heavy armoured car' adopted by the French army in 1950 and only replaced by the AMX-10RC during 1987. It soldiers on in North Africa and Portugal and may turn up elsewhere if the French sell off their surviving vehicles. It has a driver at both ends, the rear one doubling as radio operator, and the two pairs of wheels in the middle are lowered when crossing rough ground. It has an oscillating turret similar to that of the AMX-13 but no automatic loading system, which was tried but proved too heavy.

Specification:
Crew: 4
Combat weight: 13.5 tonnes
Road speed: 105 km/h
Power to weight ratio: 14.81 hp/tonne
Length: 5.56 m
Height: 2.32 m on 8 wheels, 2.24 m on 4
Armament: 1×90-mm gun; 1×7.5-mm machine-gun

Assessment
Firepower   ****
Protection   ****
Age   *****
Worldwide users   **

The EBR has been replaced in French service by the AMX-10, but Mauritania, Portugal and Tunisia are still users.

scout car variants ideal for the African and Far Eastern climates exist, including the EPR scout car with a single 12.7-mm machine-gun, the EPF border protection vehicle and EPA airfield protection vehicle, this last designed to carry a cache of 50 hand grenades as well as a fearsome array of three 7.62-mm machine-guns.

As an export vehicle, the Panhard AML has been one of the most successful creations in armoured history. Cheap and versatile, it has served the French army well and the friends of France better. There can be no doubt that the AML, in one of its numerous formats, will be in service well into the 21st century.

The SADF have greatly improved the original design, based on experience gained in actual combat. The Mk 7 has an improved engine optimised for the heat of the bush, more armour, and a new transmission that can be changed in field conditions in 40 minutes.

the AML 90 with its rivals

Saladin

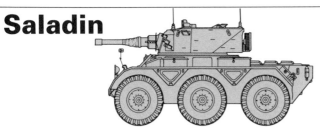

Entering production 30 years ago, the Saladin served the British Army very well in the counter-insurgency campaigns of the 1960s. Replaced in British service by the CVR(T) series, it remains in widespread use in Africa and Asia. Some war reserve stocks are reportedly maintained in the UK so if the balloon goes up the Saladin might be trundled out once more. It is not amphibious, has no NBC system and no night vision aids. The 76-mm gun fires HE, canister and a useful HESH round.

Specification:
Crew: 3
Combat weight: 11.59 tonnes
Road speed: 72 km/h
Power to weight ratio: 14.66 hp/tonne
Length: 4.93 m
Height: 2.19 m
Armament: 1×76-mm gun; 2×7.62-mm machine-guns

Assessment
Firepower	★★★★
Protection	★★★
Age	★★★★★
Worldwide users	★★★

The Saladin is a good deal heavier than the AML 90 but has a much lighter and less effective gun.

Ferret

The Ferret is a light scout car introduced in the early 1950s which served alongside the Saladin in the British Army. Although manufacture ceased in 1971 many of the 4,000 Ferrets produced remain in service, particularly in Africa. Alvis in the UK offer modernised versions of re-conditioned original Ferrets which still make a very cost-effective armoured scout car. Basic Ferrets have no NBC system, night vision kit or amphibious capability.

Specification:
(Ferret Mk 1)
Crew: 2
Combat weight: 4.2 tonnes
Road speed: 93 km/h
Power to weight ratio: 30.6 hp/tonne
Length: 3.8 m
Height: 1.9 m
Armament: 1×7.62-mm machine-gun

Assessment
Firepower	★★
Protection	★★
Age	★★★★★
Worldwide users	★★★★

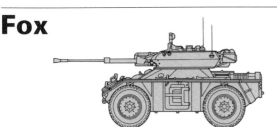

It was the success of the Ferret in British service which inspired the French to design the AML 90.

Fox

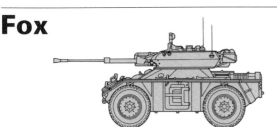

The Fox is a development of the late production Ferret. With an aluminium hull and turret and a 30-mm RARDEN cannon it offers better protection and superior firepower. It can ford up to 1 metre and can swim with a flotation screen erected. It is air transportable; three Foxes fit in a Lockheed C-130 Hercules which is to land them or two if they are to be paradropped. British Foxes have NBC detection kit and ZB 298 surveillance radar.

Specification:
Crew: 3
Combat weight: 6.1 tonnes
Road speed: 104 km/h+
Power to weight ratio: 30 hp/tonne
Length: 4.2 m
Height: 2.2 m
Armament: 1×30-mm cannon; 1×7.62-mm machine-gun

Assessment
Firepower	★★★
Protection	★★
Age	★★
Worldwide users	★

The Fox is designed to fight in a more hostile battlefield environment than the bush.

Rescued!

You've survived a lot during the last few days — enemy action, your ship sunk under you, shark attacks, and the perils of life on a hostile ocean, adrift in a flimsy rubber raft. Now you've had indications that your immediate danger is coming to an end: rescue or a landfall is imminent. But you still can't afford to relax. These last stages can be as hazardous as anything which has gone before.

So far, with the risk of attracting the attention of the enemy well in mind, you will have kept a carefully low profile, but you can now begin advertising your presence to rescuers.

A good first step is to tie together any metal containers you may have – jerry cans are ideal – and hoist them to the top of your mast, tying a square strip of cloth or bright flag, if you have

one, alongside them. One of the internationally-recognised signals for a vessel in distress or in need of assistance is a flag with a ball – or anything vaguely resembling a ball – above or below it. Suitably battered, your tins will become a 'ball', and being metallic they will also provide a focus for radar searches.

Using your radio

You can also turn the orange side of your canopy skywards, and be prepared for two or more of your crew to wave it if a friendly aircraft or ship comes into sight. And now that you are within safe distance of rescuers, you can bring your radio into play.

Obviously plain language is best used in transmitting radio signals, but you can also use Morse, or combine Morse with the International Code of

Signals (ICS); most life rafts will have a complete code book as part of the equipment.

The present ICS came into effect in 1969 and, using it, seamen of nine nations – English, French, German, Greek, Italian, Japanese, Norwegian, Russian and Spanish – can communicate with each other without knowing any foreign language. A combination of single, double or triple letter signals provides a multitude of meanings; using the triple letter section, prefixed by the letter 'M', even complex medical matters can be discussed over the air. The ICS can also be transmitted vocally using the phonetic letter spelling system – ALPHA, BRAVO, CHARLIE and so forth.

Signal pistols, flares, and smoke signals should be part of the life raft's equipment, and will come with in-

Rescued!

structions for use. Normally, rocket flares or shells showing red stars are fired one at a time at short intervals, followed by the display of hand flares giving off red or orange coloured smoke.

Don't expend flares and rockets when no ship or aircraft is in sight, or if visibility is poor; your flares will be in limited supply, and in any case you must still be cautious about attracting the enemy.

Signalling methods

During the day you may communicate between a rescuing vessel, the shore, or between rafts using signalling mirrors with the Morse code as a basis, or by hand-flags or arms; by night, use a lantern or flashlight. In bad visibility, single shots, fired at regularly-spaced intervals, will help guide a rescuer to your position. The sound of a whistle carries over long distances on a calm night at sea, and can also be used to attract attention.

Meanwhile, your look-outs will have been keeping careful watch for signs of land. A fixed cumulus cloud in a clear sky or among other moving clouds often hovers over or slightly downwind of an island, and a distant bank of cloud may indicate a shoreline.

Reflections in the sky can be indicative; in tropical areas, a greenish tint on clouds is often caused by reflections from lagoons or coral reefs, while light-coloured clouds in Arctic areas may mean icefields or snow-covered land.

The sea itself becomes lighter in colour as land draws near. Unusual smells – woodsmoke, for instance, or sounds – the roar of surf – can travel far out to sea, and the movement of birds should be watched. Seabirds are more common near land, and the direction in which they fly at dawn and dusk is a good pointer: during the day they are hunting for food and their flight is random.

Don't be fooled by mirages in the tropics, particularly at midday; viewed from slightly different heights or angles, mirages change appearance or disappear.

When land approaches, and if you decide to swim for it, wear at least one thickness of clothing and your boots or shoes, and use the energy-saving breast or side stroke. In moderate surf, ride on the back of small waves and swim forward, shallow-diving just before the wave breaks. In heavy surf, try to swim in the troughs, and when the seaward wave approaches, submerge and swim forward into the next trough, pushing off the bottom or swimming to the surface if you are caught in an undertow.

Breakers

On a rocky shore, avoid 'exploding' spray, and try to pick a spot where the waves rush up the rocks, taking your time and conserving your strength – which you will need to hang on and pull yourself clear.

Advance towards the breakers in a sitting position, on the rear of a large wave, paddling with your hands and

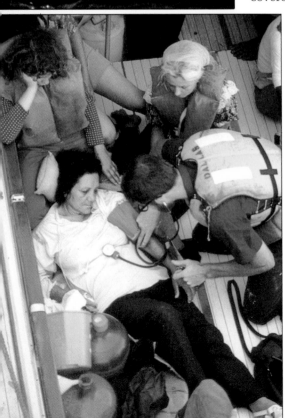

Left: Because life in a raft can quickly undermine your health, all survivors should avoid strenuous activity, which accelerates water loss. Don't ration water too tightly: people have died with water to spare. In a small raft, sea sickness can be a major problem as vomiting leads to dehydration.

Right: Rescue at last! In order to set the rescue forces into action it is crucially important to send a last radio message before your ship or aircraft sinks. If you can tell the coastguard the name of your vessel, number of people aboard, current position and nature of the emergency, you will shorten your ordeal considerably.

Being rescued by helicopter is one survival situation you cannot practise. Stay calm and follow any instructions the crew give you. Above all, don't panic if conditions do not permit the helicopter to pick you up. Once you have been located, the emergency services will not give up until you are safe.

thrusting your feet forward to absorb the shock of impact; if you don't reach shore on the first attempt, tread water until the next wave comes along, and repeat the procedure.

Crossing reefs

Use the same technique to cross rocky reefs, with your knees slightly bent and your feet together. Try to stay as relaxed as possible. Don't try to swim through patches of seaweed, but take advantage by crawling over their surface, grasping the growth with overhand movements and pulling yourself along.

If you are rafting ashore, avoid strong surf and try to manoeuvre into the lee of the promontory or island, with the sun out of your eyes, and don't attempt a landing beneath rocky cliffs or over coral reefs: your ideal landing spot, of course, will be a shelving beach. Again, take your time, and select a landing place, then take down your mast and put out the sea anchor on as long a line as possible to help keep the raft's head shorewards, and inflate your life jacket.

Divide the crew into two, one half for each side of the raft; when a heavy sea approaches, half should pull towards the sea until the crest passes, and then the other half should pull towards the shore until the next heavy sea comes along.

Righting the raft

Remember that the raft must have as much speed as possible to pass through an oncoming crest to avoid 'broaching' or turning over broadside, or being tumbled end over end; try and avoid meeting a large wave at the moment it breaks, and dropping suddenly into a trough at the other side. If the raft does capsize, grab hold and

Helicopter rescue by strop

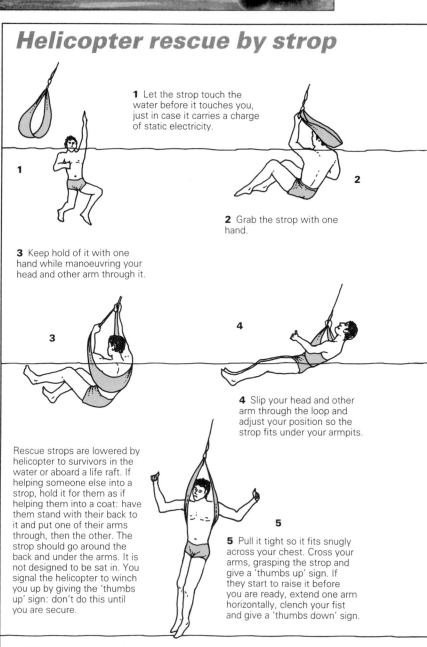

1 Let the strop touch the water before it touches you, just in case it carries a charge of static electricity.

2 Grab the strop with one hand.

3 Keep hold of it with one hand while manoeuvring your head and other arm through it.

4 Slip your head and other arm through the loop and adjust your position so the strop fits under your armpits.

Rescue strops are lowered by helicopter to survivors in the water or aboard a life raft. If helping someone else into a strop, hold it for them as if helping them into a coat: have them stand with their back to it and put one of their arms through, then the other. The strop should go around the back and under the arms. It is not designed to be sat in. You signal the helicopter to winch you up by giving the 'thumbs up' sign: don't do this until you are secure.

5 Pull it tight so it fits snugly across your chest. Cross your arms, grasping the strop and give a 'thumbs up' sign. If they start to raise it before you are ready, extend one arm horizontally, clench your fist and give a 'thumbs down' sign.

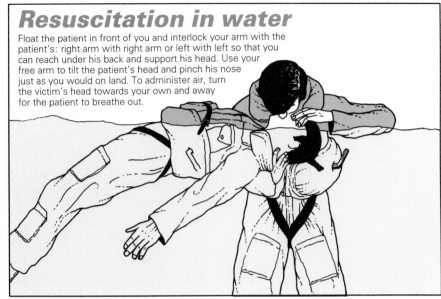

Resuscitation in water

Float the patient in front of you and interlock your arm with the patient's: right arm with right arm or left with left so that you can reach under his back and support his head. Use your free arm to tilt the patient's head and pinch his nose just as you would on land. To administer air, turn the victim's head towards your own and away for the patient to breathe out.

pilot an indication of sea level wind. Depending on conditions the approach height will usually be between 25 and 50 ft, though a Sea King, for instance, can lower a winch wire from 240 ft.

Make sure that everything movable in the raft is lashed down or firmly stowed: even a small piece of paper in a helicopter engine can cause a crash, and the downwash from the rotor will easily lift a loose life raft tarpaulin. *Never* try to grab the winch wire with your bare hands; it can build up a

If you are discovered by a ship, your rescuers may launch a ship's boat. Keep your wits about you if the weather conditions are poor: don't switch off now that someone else is here. You are not home and dry until you're on the ship.

stay with it; in any case stay aboard until it grounds, and then leap out and lift it clear of the water – don't drag it.

In Arctic waters you may encounter large ice floes suitable for landing on, but avoid rubbing the raft against the edge of the ice, and once on the floe keep the raft inflated and ready, as the floe may break up suddenly. Avoid icebergs, which may capsize, however large, and smaller floes which may be disintegrating.

Shipwreck shelters

Many apparently inhospitable mainland shorelines in the Arctic region have shelters for shipwrecked mariners. The Iceland National Life Saving Association has an elaborate system of shelters equipped with either radio-transmitters or telephone, flares and rockets, food, clothing, medical supplies and fuel dotted all around the coast.

Rescue by air may take the form of a fixed wing aircraft 'pointing' you in the direction of shore or towards a rescue craft below the horizon, or by helicopter.

If for some reason you cannot communicate with the aircraft by radio, but he has spotted you, the pilot will usually circle two or three times and then either open and close the throttle or, in the case of a piston-engined aircraft, change the airscrew pitch to indicate by the changing engine tone that he has you in vision, and then will fly off at low altitude in the direction of your potential rescuer. He may repeat the manoeuvre.

Flare signals

At night the aircraft will drop green flares at between three and five thousand feet at about five-minute intervals. You should reply with a red flare, *once the green light has died out*. Fire another red flare after about twenty seconds, to allow the aircraft to line up on your bearing, and a third when the aircraft is overhead, or if it appears to be going badly off course.

In the case of helicopter rescue, the craft will approach you from astern, heading into the relative wind direction; either fire a smoke flare or hold up a streamer or pennant to give the

lethal charge of static electricity which the pilot will discharge by dipping the wire into the sea. And never try to secure the end of the winch wire to the raft.

Royal Navy SAR helicopters usually carry a diver who may enter the water and superintend the lifting of survivors; his instructions should be followed exactly and as quickly as possible, as time may be precious. In this case survivors are usually lifted by double lift in a strop or rope sling, with the diver accompanying them in a canvas seat.

In other circumstances it may be necessary for the survivor to position the strop himself, and give the 'thumbs up' signal when ready to be hoisted. Injured persons can be strapped into a special lightweight stretcher carried by the helicopter.

Finally, always remember to do precisely what you are told by a rescue helicopter crew; they are as expert in their field as you are in yours – and it would be the height of irony to have survived perilous days in a life raft only to step from the rescue helicopter and straight into a whirling rotor blade!

Hypo-thermia

This table gives the median survival time according to the temperature and your action in the water. Note how much faster you lose heat by swimming and how the HELP posture and huddling will help keep you alive.

time in hours

- huddle
- HELP position
- floating with flotation device e.g. lifejacket
- treading water
- swimming

temperature in degrees F

20 — 15 — 10 — 5

25   35   45   55   65 70

Seashore Food

Conservation

1 Never take excessive quantities of any of these wild foods.
2 Always cut seaweed rather than pull it up.
3 Do not take undersized molluscs or crustaceans.
4 Leave some roots of a plant for regrowth.
5 If a plant has gone to seed, scatter the seeds for next year's growth.
6 Do not kill birds or take their eggs: buy an unplucked chicken from the butcher and practise on that. Likewise, the fishmonger should be your source of most shellfish and fish.

The coastline offers the survivor a wide variety of food sources if you know what to look for. The major problem is a psychological one: you may have to eat some fairly unappetising items. The essential precaution is to learn as much as you can about the subject first. By familiarising yourself with the food sources the seashore has to offer and trying some of the techniques described below, you will be able to overcome your initial reluctance. Then if you find yourself in a survival situation near the coast, you have already won half the battle.

Drinking water is always one of the survivor's top priorities. By digging a shallow well just above the high water level you will be able to collect fresh (if a little brackish) water. Don't dig too deep, or the sea will seep in. This is a good technique to practise next time you visit a beach. If you have a vessel to boil water in, boil sea water and collect the steam in a clean cotton cloth. Squeeze out the cloth and you have distilled, drinkable water. Now it is time to forage for food.

The coastline is abundant with food sources, but there are a few basic rules to remember to avoid food poisoning or contamination from all the waste man so thoughtfully dumps into the sea. The edible items discussed here are all standard European shore life;

The seashore can provide a rich harvest for the survivor, but not much of it is very appetising or instantly recognisable as edible. People have starved to death just because they could not bring themselves to eat the food available.

tropical beaches are more abundant but so are the dangers. The basic rules are:

1 Don't eat anything too brightly coloured red, yellow or green. It is a natural sign of poison being present.
2 Don't eat any items washed up or away from their natural environment.
3 Avoid anything with a very strong smell.
4 If in doubt, don't eat it.

Checklist for seashore edibles

1 Don't collect mussels near a sewage outlet.
2 Avoid areas of oil or chemical pollution, e.g. busy harbours or industrial sites, or stagnant pools left by very high tides.
3 Avoid dead fish, crustaceans, molluscs or seaweeds left by the tide.
4 Don't eat jellyfish.
5 Don't eat spiny fish or those with bony skins instead of proper scales (but these can do for bait, of course).
6 Don't eat large quantities of seaweed all at once. It can have the same effect as a massive Vindaloo, which is bad news normally and doubly bad in a survival situation.

Cockle *(Cardium edule)*
Widely distributed along British coasts, they are normally found 25-75mm beneath the surface of the beach. Wash off the mud and sand and stand in clean water for at least six hours. Drop into a pan of boiling water and simmer for five minutes. Eat on their own or with soup.

Clam *(Mya arenia)* **(Below)**
Common in the middle and lower shore, clams look like large mussels and can be up to 10-13cm across. Wash thoroughly as for cockles and scald for 10 minutes. Remove the meat from the shell and cut syphons off. The remaining meat should then be fried or baked for 30 minutes or boiled until tender.

Preparing seashore edibles

1 Test mussels by sideways pressure: if the animal is alive you will feel some resistance.
2 Other shellfish are tested by forcing the shell open a fraction of an inch. If alive and well it will shut again quickly once you release the pressure. If it is already open, opens wide with ease or fails to shut again, it is safer to assume the thing is dead and that you should not eat it.
3 Always wash seashore edibles in plenty of fresh water. Shellfish should be left to stand in clean water overnight if possible. Check they are still alive when you come to cook them: a single dead one will contaminate the rest of your meal.
4 Always cook thoroughly to kill bacteria that are naturally present.

Shellfish

Only eat shellfish you find alive; dead ones can be used as bait. Bivalve molluscs feed by filtering food particles out of the water. They also filter out and retain bacteria which, in warm weather, multiply and can cause food poisoning to humans. This is especially true of mussels and oysters, which filter large quantities of water daily and relish the warm, soupy conditions near sewage outlets.

Scallops or clams *(Pecten maximus)* **(Above)**
These are the classic shells we all recognise; found on the lower shore, they are only uncovered at very low tides. Like clams, they require a lot of cooking. Wash and scald, cut away the white and orange flesh and fry or boil until cooked.

Whelk *(Buccinum undatum)* **(Above)**
This is the largest of the gastropods (coiled shells). They are very meaty, but require a great deal of boiling otherwise you will still be chewing on the same whelk hours later. Like the smaller winkle, they can be found in rock pools and among seaweed.

Limpet *(Patella vulgata)*
Found on rocks below high water, limpets should be soaked for about six hours then boiled for five minutes. They can be rather tough, but further boiling will tenderise them.

Mussels *(Mytilus edulis)* **(Below)**
Commonest of British shellfish, these are delicious but you must exercise considerable caution when collecting them. They are responsible for most cases of shellfish poisoning. Stand in at least two changes of fresh water and check carefully that each one is alive before cooking. They can be boiled, or baked in ashes.

Winkle *(Littorina littorea)* **(Above)**
A small, spiral-shaped pointed shell, normally dark grey in colour, you will need a large number of them for a decent meal. Soak them in fresh water to clear them of sand, then plunge into boiling water for about 10 minutes. Extract the meat with the proverbial winkle pin.

Fish

Fish can often be found in pools at low tide around the bases of rocks and under clumps of weed, and eels and small fish are often left behind by the tide. A great deal of fluid is stored in the flesh and the spine cavity of fish and, surprisingly, this is not salty. Hunting fish in pools is not easy: traps and spears will both work, but only if you have practised first. A maze trap works well for flatfish and others in coastal areas. It should be about 2-2½ metres across with a mouth of 40-50cm. The outer walls of wood or stones should project 60cm or so into the trap. Avoid small, spiny fish, which are likely to be poisonous.

Fish can be boiled, roasted in a fire, baked in clay or cooked on a spit. Prepare them by cutting off the heads, removing the guts and cleaning them out. A very sharp survival knife is an essential item here. Small fish can be eaten whole without cleaning. Never eat a fish with a suspiciously powerful odour, slimy skin, sunken eyes or flabby skin. If you feel there's something fishy about it, prod it with your thumb: if it remains dented, do not eat it. Use it for bait instead.

Rock pool fish look horrible but are edible, although a bit bony. They grow up to about 15cm in length and are well camouflaged, so you have to search hard under weeds and rocks. Beware the varieties that have spines around the gills; they can give you very nasty cuts. Use a net or a line with baited hook.

Seaweeds

Most seaweeds are edible raw or cooked, and they form a valuable addition to your diet providing your water supply is adequate, because they tend to make you thirsty. They are found in inshore waters and are found attached to rocks at low water. In addition to general rules, there are three specific rules concerning seaweed:

1 Only eat fresh, healthy specimens. Eat nothing with strong odours or flavour: they should be firm to the touch, not wilted, slimy nor fishy-smelling.
2 Do not eat threadlike or slender forms. Sea sorrels contain small amounts of sulphuric acid which can severely upset your stomach. They betray their presence by bleaching out other plants nearby. The test, if you are not sure what you've found, is to crush a little of it in your hand. The released acid will make the plant decay quickly and in 5-10 minutes it will give off an unpleasant odour.
3 Inspect seaweed carefully and shake out any small organisms, e.g. tiny crabs.

There are many types of seaweed. Those found in the UK include:

Entomorphia intestinalis
(Above)
A mouthful to say but a satisfactory mouthful to eat, this is widely distributed around the UK and can be eaten raw or dried and used in soups.

Laver
Found on the Atlantic, Pacific and Mediterranean coasts, this is plentiful around the UK and is eaten in Wales. A thin, leaflike transparent membrane with fine, wavy flat fronds, it is red, purple and brown in colour. Cut just above the base so that you don't kill the plant off. Wash it thoroughly to remove grit, and simmer slowly. It can be eaten like spinach or rolled into balls, dipped in breadcrumbs and fried. If survival cuisine is beyond you, you can still eat it raw.

Bladder wrack
Fresh or dry fronds may be used, boiled in soups or stews. It can also be dried to make tea of a sort.

Carragheen (Irish moss)
This is found on the rockier Atlantic shores. Tough, leathery and many-branched, it is red/purple to purple/brown. Boil it and eat stewed with fish, meat or other vegetables.

Sea lettuce
Found in the Atlantic and Pacific, this is lettuce-like in appearance and is coloured light to dark green. It may be eaten raw or used as a vegetable.

Crustaceans

These are a major food source but also a common cause of food poisoning, so proceed with caution. Never eat a raw crustacean. Cook them by covering with sand and earth and building a fire over the pile: they will cook in their own juices. A better way is to boil them in water.

Crabs, crayfish, lobsters, shrimps and prawns are found throughout the world and all are edible. They go off quickly, so eat them soon after catching them. Boil some water, insert crustacean, and eat 20-30 minutes later.

All crabs are edible, but the 'edible crab' has far more meat in the body and claws and is generally pink. Boil the crab whole but do not eat the 'dead men's fingers' inside the crab as these are poisonous. They are in a separate section to the edible flesh.

Right: Lobsters can be caught in home-made lobster pots, which should be anchored in about 2 metres of water at low tide and baited with crushed crab. They should be boiled whole.

In the past people have eaten sea birds such as puffins and gannets, which were harvested in the Hebrides until the 1960s. They are very oily and taste revolting, but could be eaten during a wartime survival situation. The puffin is now a protected species and any attempt to eat one will leave you open to prosecution.

The common octopus
(Octopus vulgaris) (Below)
You may be able to spear octopus amongst the rocks, but the better method is to leave out large tin cans or sections of pipe with a few stones secured to the bottom just below the low tide mark. Octopi will adopt these containers as lairs when they move in at high tide: they will form the stones into a wall at the open end of the tin. The only real problem is getting the octopus out of the tin.

Birds
All sea birds are edible, either raw or cooked, although some may taste a little peculiar. Roasting and baking in clay are good ways of cooking, but boiling is most nutritious as you retain all the juices. Before cooking, a bird should be bled and drawn and the feathers removed, although a small bird can be rolled in clay and baked: the feathers and skin come away when cooked. The livers are particularly good, and the entrails make good bait for fishing. **Do not attempt to kill or eat any bird unless you are in a genuine wartime survival situation.**

Below: Birds' eggs, such as these gull eggs, are good eating for the survivor. But taking birds' eggs outside a survival situation is not only grossly irresponsible but illegal.

Left: The common octopus, when threatened, will squirt out vast quantities of dye, which is harmless. Octopus is very tough unless you tenderise it on a rock beforehand. You can boil it, but it is far better fried.

Other food sources
Other possible food sources include sea urchins, sea cucumbers, starfish, razor shells and lug worms. And don't forget that the seashore will be inhabited by dune-dwelling creatures such as mice, rabbits and lizards: all these can go in the survivor's pot. As in all survival situations, living on the seashore is all about making the maximum use of whatever is available.

Shoreline plants

There are a few plants found along the shore which can provide the survivor with quite reasonable food.

Sea Beet *(Beta vulgaris)*
Also known as wild spinach, this was the ancestor of our beetroot, sugar beet and spinach. The leaves may be picked from spring to autumn. They are full of natural minerals, especially iron and vitamins A and C. Wash the leaves well and remove the thicker stalks before boiling in a very little water. Better still, steam it for about 10 minutes.

Marsh samphire *(Salicornia)*
This thrives in salty marshlands along the foreshores of Britain and has been described as the next best thing to asparagus. Ready from the longest day in June to the last day of August, the young shoots can be eaten raw in salads or cooked in a little boiling water. Drain and add a little butter and pepper if you have any. Eat by stripping the soft flesh away from the hard, spiny stems with your teeth. Marsh samphire now appears on some restaurant menus in East Anglia as a delicacy.

Sea kale *(Crambe maritima)*
A cabbage-like plant growing in large clumps with huge, fleshy grey/green leaves, it is found in shingle, sand dunes and along cliffs on north temperate coasts and it was known to the Romans, who preserved it in barrels for long sea journeys. Pick young leaves and white underground shoots from February to May. Boil briefly, chop and boil for a further 20 minutes in changed water. They can also be steamed or baked.

Sea arrow grass *(Triglochin maritima)*
Found near north temperate coasts, salt marshes and grassy foreshore areas, this can be eaten raw but is best added to soups or boiled as a vegetable.

Fighting Fit

Exercise Final Fling

Exercise Final Fling really puts you on the spot. The platoon commander issues his orders for the attack and, as a section commander, you have to brief your section for the operation. It's down to you to translate the Commander's instructions into orders to your section, and your responsibility to ensure that the men under your command understand the plan.

Week Five of the Battle Course is taken up with Exercise Final Fling, held on the Sennybridge Training Area. For this you need to remember, and use, everything you've been taught during the course so far. Much of the exercise is taken up by patrols, attacks and ambushes.

All of them call for prior briefings, or orders. These are an important part of a section commander's training, and each and every one of you must satisfy your SIs that you are able to explain to your men all the details of an impending operation.

Basically, the platoon commander will tell you – the section commander

The Section Commanders Battle Course is also a lesson in co-operation: while the appointed section commanders prepare their orders, the rest of you help prepare the scoff or work on the model of the operational area.

in general and in detail. If he has not seen the area of the objective, a section commander will hand over to someone who has – say the lead scout of a recent recce patrol. He will fire first-hand information on the target, before the section commander continues with the *situation*.

This part tells everyone vital details about enemy and friendly forces: attachments and detachments, and any civilians or refugees likely to be in the area.

Next comes the *mission,* explained in just one sentence: "Our mission is to destroy all the enemy in the observation post at grid . . ."

Execution

To make sure that everyone fully understands, the mission is always repeated. Then comes the *execution,* a long and detailed briefing:

"This will be a five phase operation. Phase one will be the route out, up to and including confirmation of the forward rendezvous (FRV) . . ."

Other phases are: action in the FRV; action on the objective; withdrawal to the FRV and action at the FRV; the route back.

When you've introduced the five phases, you give a detailed explanation of each one:

"Phase one: the route out. We will be moving from here, through a series of RVs. Look at the route card . . . Leg one will be from here to the corner of the wood at . . ."

Each phase deals with all the essential details that those taking part in the patrol need to know. Although you

Now you explain the plan to your men, using a scale model of the area. You have a lot of information to get over and it will take a good half hour to complete the briefing. Don't deliver the whole thing in a flat monotone, or the audience will switch off and miss something vital.

have a reminder to help you with the briefing, it provides only the headings and sub-headings to be explained. It is up to you to fill in the details.

There is a lot to cover. For example, during phase three, 'Action on the objective', you are expected to inform the cover fire group of its composition; task; position; route; formation; arcs of fire; signals for opening fire; action to take if discovered by the enemy;

– *what* he wants. It is then up to you to tell your men *how* to carry out the task. The simplest set of orders is probably that for a fighting patrol.

You will be given all the available information, plus anything found out from the most recent reconnaissance missions, on your task. You will normally have at least two hours to prepare for your delivery of orders. In this time you'll also need to construct a model of the operational area. You must be ready for your orders group ('O group') at a time designated by the platoon commander, with your men seated in their order of march around the model.

The *preliminaries* are just that. You describe the model and give such general information as map co-ordinates, weather and moonstate, and times of first and last light.

The second stage covers the *ground*

Pointing out the route the unit will take as it moves towards the target. You have to make sure everyone has understood what is supposed to happen. Previously you've only been on the receiving end of this sort of briefing.

Fighting Fit

and action to take if separated from the main group!

Need to know

You must similarly brief the close recce/assault group and the FRV protection group. Put yourself in their position – which is exactly where you were until very recently. *You* would want to know everything possible about an operation.

After explaining the five phases of the execution of the mission, you can move on to the *co-ordinating instructions:* "You've all been fed, and you've had a couple of hours' gonk, so we'll be moving out of here immediately after rehearsals . . ."

This stage of the briefing deals with timings; meals; rehearsals; action on halts and lights; the fireplan and similar details.

Next comes the *summary of execution* – essentially an overall appreciation of the operation, provided in your own words. *Service support* comes next; and has eight sub-headings: dress; equipment; weapons; ammunition; rations; medical; prisoners of war; and transport.

Then come *command and signals:* ". . . Platoon HQ will be at this location. However, after 0400 it will move to grid . . . On the route out, my position will be the third man in from the front . . ."

This, the final part, includes details of the debrief and any passwords or passnumbers to be used. As with the other main headings, you finish with the usual "Any questions?"

If there are none, you can make sure that the briefing has sunk in by asking a few questions yourself. The O group concludes with everyone synchronising their watches with yours.

Keeping dark

Assuming that you are suitably concealed beneath a wood or similar cover, you can give daylight orders with the section sitting around the model of the area of operations. At night, however, you need to build a light-proof shelter – a type of low basha, made from several ponchos secured so that the section commander can freely use his torch to illuminate the model, or a map, without the risk of any light escaping and

Briefing in daylight under cover of the trees is much easier than briefing at night. Then you must talk the men through the model by torchlight in a lightproof basha.

compromising your position. The only problem with the light-proof shelter is that it results in loss of night vision. So, before moving out, you need to leave sufficient time for everyone's eyesight to re-adjust to the darkness.

A good point to remember when delivering orders is to moderate your voice. It can take half an hour or more to explain an operation, and a flat, monotonous tone will soon have your audience nodding off to sleep. Briefings are vital to the success of a mission, so you must make them sound interesting in order to hold the full attention of those involved. Their lives, and yours, will depend on it!

Above: The acid test of your orders – the section overruns the 'enemy' position, slaughtering the men in fur hats and taking the objective. Your job as section commander is, of course, only half done – the withdrawal phase is yet to come!

Right: The 'enemy' dead are quickly searched for any useful intelligence. If the section is to get it right on the day, there is no substitute for a full rehearsal before the operation. This helps fix the drills in everybody's minds so they are second nature.

Combat Report
Palestine:
Manshiya Quarter Fighting Part 1

A subaltern with 1st Battalion The Argyll and Sutherland Highlanders served in Palestine in February 1948 as the British Mandate was drawing to an end. He tells the story of a struggle with a Jewish strongpoint.

Since the United Nations declaration of Partition for Palestine at the end of November 1947, many areas throughout the country had become a no-man's land. One such place was the Manshiya Quarter, a narrow neck of houses which ran between the Jewish city of Tel Aviv and the Arab capital of Jaffa, where fierce fighting had broken out between Arabs and Jews. The British Army and the police endeavoured to keep the peace and to make sure that our own lines of withdrawal from the country would be kept open.

I was commanding a platoon at that time, but was also second-in-command of 'D' Company. One day at our base in Jaffa I was told to get some soldiers and make my way as quickly as possible to the Manshiya police station, which was under attack. I had a section of 10 men on standby, so we jumped into a vehicle and hurried over there.

A direct hit

As we arrived an ugly whiplash of bullets snapped along the narrow street, and was returned by small-arms fire from the police station nearby. Above all this came the even more chilling sound of screaming and wailing from the Arab women as they carried two dead men into a nearby house.

We made our way into the police station and went straight to the sandbagged loopholes to return fire, which was coming from a building a few hundred yards away. It was heavily sandbagged and surrounded by barbed wire: a Jewish strongpoint.

The skirmish had started very suddenly when two unarmed civilian Arabs were shot dead as they walked past the police station. Each took a bullet through the head. The police station was fired on at the same time; the police inside returned fire, but being low in numbers and half expecting a Jewish assault, they called for assistance. Tom McCallister, a subaltern with 'B' company, turned up with another section just after we got there.

Some of the weapons recovered from the Jewish strongpoint after our assault. The position was rushed before dawn, and the defenders didn't know what was happening until it was too late.

We took careful aim, but our fire seemed to have little effect. The Jewish fire was pretty accurate and a number of their rounds thudded into the sandbags near my head, which was somewhat disconcerting.

Tom McCallister's men had a PIAT (Projector Infantry Anti-Tank) with them, a useful weapon against tanks or buildings. Tom grabbed the weapon and I grabbed a container of six bombs, and we made our way through the ruined buildings to the right of the police station. We ended up on a first floor balcony, where we had an excellent view of the Jewish strongpoint. I loaded and Tom fired – a direct hit on the sandbagged fort! We repeated the exercise.

I always carried my camera with me, and as the second PIAT bomb struck I rashly stood up and took a picture. Jewish rounds smashed into the wall just behind me, showering us with plaster. It was fortunate that I wasn't hit, but I did get a good photograph!

We fired the remaining bombs, and the opposition's fire noticeably slackened. We were told later that we had killed six men and wounded several others.

Our blood was up and we now wanted to take the strongpoint, but our headquarters wisely ordered us to break off and return to base, and some reinforcements arrived to spend the night at the station. A well-organised assault on the Jewish position was to be made in a day or so.

Two days later, we received our orders and then carefully briefed our men and prepared weapons and ammunition.

"Let's go, chaps!"

We were to move before dawn and take up positions on the flat roofs near the strongpoint. From there we could direct all our fire on to the objective if necessary. The assault was to be undertaken by a platoon from 'B' Company, led by a giant Highlander named Donald Bruce.

Complete silence was ordered, in the hope that we might take them by surprise. At dawn, Donald and his men would dash up the narrow street where the two Arabs had died, and get into the Jewish position. If any firing started, our company was to plaster the position with every weapon available. A detachment of Royal Engineers stood by in support.

We rose in the early hours of the morning to find it steadily pouring with rain. Annoying, but good cover. We slowly made our way through the rubble-strewn streets and got into our fire positions on the tops of the buildings. I was on the extreme left of the company, and I knew that below me crouched Donald Bruce and his assault group. I thought what a mess it would be if the enemy were alert and sent a storm of steel down on Donald's men. There would be nowhere to escape to, and even our company firepower would probably not stop one determined man firing from behind cover.

It began to lighten a little, but the rain still fell steadily. It would soon be time. I heard Donald's hoarse, 'Let's go, chaps!' followed by the scrunch of boots below. My safety catch went forward, as did everyone else's. Then we waited with bated breath for the first round of fire from the strongpoint. None came! The assault group were soon through the wire and into the position. Within a remarkably short time, a green Very light arched up into the gloom – the success signal.

A line of prisoners

Shortly after this, a line of unhappy-looking prisoners, with their hands in the air, came stumbling over the rubble near the strongpoint. Donald and his platoon had achieved complete surprise, and had managed to get right into the strongpoint before anyone had realised that they were there. A search of the position revealed light machine-gins, rifles, grenades and large quantities of ammunition. In all, 18 prisoners were taken. Amazingly, there were no casualties.

The Royal Engineers then moved in, and after about an hour my company was told to move back. Shortly after we withdrew there was the most tremendous explosion, and the strongpoint disappeared in smoke and debris. The Sappers had done their work.

Then we marched back to base to clean up a bit and enjoy a well-earned breakfast. Our morale was high, despite the continuing rain. Later that day at our headquarters I saw the young Sapper officer and complimented him on the destruction of the building. He gave me a rather wry smile and replied. ''Well, several buildings nearby also fell down, so there were a few complaints. But I wanted to make absolutely certain, so I used rather more explosive for the job than is laid down in regulations!''

The PIAT (Projector Infantry Anti-Tank) bomb explodes on the strongpoint. As I stood up to take this picture, bullets promptly thudded into the wall above. Once the PIAT bombs had been fired into the target the fire slackened off.

Ambush!

On the Saturday morning of Week Five your platoon leaves the shelter of the forest and clambers aboard two waiting four-tonners. It is another unusually hot day, and the instructors have kindly removed the vehicles' canvas covers and let down the metal sides so that you can enjoy a cooling breeze on the journey. Either that, or maybe – just maybe – it indicates that you are going to drive into an ambush!

The short ride takes you out of one forestry block into another. You follow a hard-baked, dusty track, flanked on one side by a slight decline, and on the right by high ground, sloping gently into the dense forest.

Eyes peeled

Everyone is alert and constantly scanning the surrounding country-side. Well, you think, if we were going to run into an ambush, this would be an ideal ...

"There they are! There they are! Fifty metres away, right hand bank!"

The firing begins. Bloody hell! Where *are* they? Okay, seen! An enemy trooper, apparently not expecting your convoy so soon, is caught sunbathing, and fumbles for

An enemy 30-calibre Browning machine-gun blazes away at the lead vehicle. It is essential that you get out and away from the vehicle and into cover. Watch out, as a switched-on enemy will mine the obvious places to go to ground.

his weapon. As the lead vehicle lurches to a sudden halt, you join everyone in the mad scramble to get

pants debus and make for the wooded rise to counter-attack.

Your men move into position under cover of the forest, then launch their assault. The enemy are soon overcome.

After the enemy dead are searched, you form up on the road, ready to continue with your interrupted journey. But – surprise, surprise – both four-tonners have been 'written off' in the ambush. Can't we get two replacements? Well, probably, but in the time it would take, you could walk the rest of the way.

It's three miles to the next harbour position – not a great distance, but far enough when you are wearing heavy kit in such warm weather.

Confusing orders

That afternoon, the platoon commander issues his orders for section anti-armour ambushes to take place in the early hours of the following morning. The appointed section commanders begin their orders at 2000. Twenty minutes into the briefing, the forest echoes to a single, thunderous explosion. It is followed by a stunned silence. Huddled around their models of the area, everyone exchanges puzzled glances. What on earth was that? There is another loud bang.

"We're under attack!"

Suddenly, everybody is reacting. Section commanders destroy all evi-

The only way to counter a vehicle ambush is by fast, aggressive action. That means getting out of the killing area and putting rounds down on the enemy with everything you have, including 66-mm LAW and white phosphorus, while the assault group put a flanking attack in on the ambush position.

Below: On the thumbs-up from the crewman, the two sticks dash for the Puma – the only painless way to see the training area. The stick commanders stop by the doors and help the rest of the stick in before clambering aboard themselves.

Once the enemy dead have been searched, kicked and counted, you have yet another tab in front of you, carrying full marching order as every truck was knocked out in the ambush. Life can be hard, especially if you happen to be no. 1 on the 84-mm today.

dence of their O Group. Bergens and support weapons are snatched up.

"Come on, *let's go!*"

You tear through the trees, downhill to a forest track, and take another tab – this time to a loading up point (LUP) close to the site of the planned ambush.

Despite having to 'bug out' in the middle of your orders, the section commanders soon regain control. The ambush is still set on time, by 0530, and you spring it an hour later. As the

The flanking attack rolls up the ambush from the right, supported by fire from the survivors of the front two vehicles. This linear ambush is no problem, but beware the enemy that puts out flank and rear protection parties.

clear, leaping off the side and rushing for cover below the bank on your left. Behind you, the second truck's occu-

Fighting Fit

The Puma touches down and you pile out to cover your arcs. As soon as the helicopter lifts off you are up and running: you do not want to get caught in the open on the LS.

An enemy rifleman firing from the cover of a bund line is swiftly dealt with in a bayonet charge after some very hot and sweaty fire-and-manoeuvre.

surviving enemy attempt to retaliate, you take advantage of their confusion, withdrawing deep into the forest.

Into the air

Later that morning, each section has to dump its Bergens on the back of a four-tonner. Then you settle down to wait for a Royal Air Force Puma for the first of three heli-assaults.

The big machine finally arrives, landing in a nearby quarry in a great, swirling cloud of dust. It takes three lifts to move the platoon into position for the first attack. When everyone is ready, one section covers the other two as they move in against a small detachment of enemy troops sheltering along a bunch line in an otherwise open area.

The attack doesn't take long, and most of you feel that it went fairly smoothly in spite of the odd hiccup. The SIs, however, share a different view:

"There was far too much for me to do there . . . Too much f**ing shouting . . .!"

"The fire positions were crap . . . Some of you couldn't even *see* the enemy!"

It's a bit late to make such basic mistakes. You listen to the criticism, determined to do better next time.

Missing persons

The second attack goes off without a hitch . . . mainly because the enemy are not where you expected them to

be. The assaulting sections sweep through the area unopposed. What a sly move! You are impressed that the instructors should trick you like this – even going so far as to use a helicopter to transport you into position, and all for nothing. In fact, the "enemy" simply fouled up. They *should* have been there – but they ended up somewhere else! Oh well, these things happen in war . . .

The third and final assault is, unfortunately, as poor as the first. Each objective is taken out, but not to the satisfaction of your instructors. One of them sums up his de-brief thus:

Above: The platoon commander marshals the Puma for the next lift. He keeps the bright orange air panel inside his smock and only opens it when the Puma appears. Who wants to stand in the middle of a field with a big orange blob on his chest with enemy about?

Right: The next helicopter insertion is slightly more strenuous: hand over hand down a 30-ft rope and carrying your fighting order and all the extra kit for a tank ambush.

". . . There was poor participation by those not in command . . . Poor comms . . . Poor fire positions . . . Poor supporting fire . . . One of you jumped in front of his own man who was putting down suppressive fire . . .!"

You glumly stare at the ground as the Colour Sergeant ends his tirade. He walks away and pauses, standing alone for a few seconds before returning.

"Okay", he says, looking slightly amused.

"I've calmed down. Now, something to cheer you up. The chopper will be back soon. You'll be pleased to know that when you get to the next destination, the chopper will not be landing. You'll be roping in from about 15 feet . . .!"

Great!

Combat Report

Palestine:
Manshiya Quarter Fighting Part 2

British Army reinforcements arrive in Jerusalem to protect the evacuation of personnel from Palestine. Infantry patrols were no longer adequate.

A subaltern with The Argyll and Sutherland Highlanders tells of further incidents in Palestine at the time of Partition in 1948.

The hand grenade exploded very close to us, and pieces of shrapnel struck the buildings nearby. We flung ourselves down, and as we did so I heard the clatter of a second grenade hitting the street. But this one failed to explode. There was complete silence . . .

We tried to peer through the darkness to see where the grenade had been thrown from, but it was impossible. The bomb thrower was probably well away by now, but we checked everywhere anyway.

I found the unexploded grenade using a shaded torch. It was home-made and the short fuse had gone out, hence its failure to explode. I slipped it into my pouch and we continued our patrol.

Later, in my billet back at our base in Jaffa, the Arab capital, I examined it in more detail. It was filled with explosive, old nails and scrap-metal – nasty! The container was an old fruit salts tin, and the writing on it stated that "one of these should be in every bedroom, bathroom and railway carriage".

Tracer criss-crossed the skies

Between Jaffa and Tel Aviv ran the Manshiya Quarter, the old section of buildings that had seen savage fighting between Jews and Arabs since the end of 1947. Many buildings had been destroyed by explosives, and each side had a line of defensive positions facing out onto the no-man's land of wrecked streets.

Our task was to try to stop, or at least damp down, the fighting. We did this by a series of

patrols. Most of the clashes took place at night, when both sides would start quite serious battles. Also, the Arabs had infiltrated small units of the Iraqi army into Jaffa, and they sometimes led the Arab irregulars in fierce attacks on Jewish positions.

We had two companies stationed in the police cantonment – roughly 200 men. But frequently, during the big night battles, several hundred men would be involved, and we could not contain the action. In these cases we manned our defensive positions in case of any attack directly on us.

A fantastic amount of ammunition was fired by both sides during these battles, and tracer criss-crossed the sky for hours while mortar bombs, hand grenades and other explosives shook the night. Strangely, there never seemed to be many casualties, although of course both factions hid their wounded so that the authorities wouldn't find them.

A nasty wound

On one such night of noisy fighting, an Iraqi force was attacking across the Jaffa-Jerusalem road towards Tel Aviv, near where we had an Army roadblock staffed by a few men. The noise was terrific, and we stayed at our posts and awaited orders.

We had recently received a draft of young National Servicemen straight from their training centre. One of these boys was in my platoon and, delighted at the brilliant firework display, he climbed up onto one of the flat roofs in order to get a better view.

He was shot, receiving a nasty wound in his thigh. He was in pain and shock when we discovered him, and we had great difficulty getting him down. Our doctor patched him up, but said he must be taken to the hospital 10 miles away as soon as possible.

Just then, I was ordered to take my platoon

This armoured truck was ambushed in the Sheik Jarrah quarter of Jerusalem. The vehicle lost control when shot at and crashed into a wall.

and hurry to our roadblock, which was under attack. On arrival we found the incumbents crouching nervously in their trenches as a fierce battle swirled around them. There were a lot of bullets cracking overhead and nearby, but as I sited my platoon it became obvious that it wasn't the block that was under fire: the Arabs were attacking across the road just north of us.

No sooner were we in position than two Bren gun carriers and our ambulance came clattering in from the city. They stopped at the block, and we pointed out that if they wanted to carry on they would have to go through the battle zone.

Then the firing slackened a bit, and as the casualty in the ambulance (the wounded soldier from my platoon) had to be got to hospital quickly, the sergeant bravely decided to press on. We wished them luck, and with one carrier ahead of the ambulance and one behind, they set off up the road.

Suddenly, all hell broke loose as scores of figures fired from the darkness at the vehicles. Tracer lashed across the road, and we could hear the heavy clangs as bullets struck the armoured Bren carriers. Finally the vehicles managed to get through the combat area, and the noise of their engines faded away in the distance.

We found out later that the ambulance had been riddled with bullets during those few minutes, but the only casualty was my already wounded private, who was hit in his other leg. It certainly wasn't his day. He survived, but never returned to the 1st Battalion!

A wounded Jewish fighter lies behind an armoured car after British troops intervened to stop one of the regular gun battles in February 1948.

Flying Picquet

Above: An 'enemy' vehicle arrives in front of your positions, signalling the end of the defensive phase of the exercise. Note how the GPMG gunner keeps his belt off the ground to keep it free from mud. From 2100 hrs you have been in NBC medium, so you all know what's coming next . . .

Left: Soaking wet equipment reflects the light from the flash as the rain pours into your new home. After 15 hours digging the trenches, you stand sentry while recce patrols vanish into the night in search of enemy armour.

Only a few more days of the course to go – and at 2100 hrs on Sunday night, you begin digging in. You have until midday, on Monday, to finish. Fifteen hours. All infantry hate this aspect of their job, and the back-breaking, blistering work is hard enough for those who have done it all before. It's perhaps tougher for those candidates from mechanised units!

Stony ground

By 1200, most of you succeed in completing your fire-trenches, but one group of four has barely made an impression in the earth. Unfortunately, they have been positioned along a particularly rocky ridge. After spit-locking the eight-yard-long trench, they average just one inch every hour! The rest of you take turns to assist, but it proves impossible to

dig any faster. By 1430 the ditch is about 18 inches at its deepest. The platoon commander tells you to stop digging further and get some rest instead.

Those who can, get their heads down. For many, though, there are sentry duties to mount and, at 1500, section recce patrols for yet another anti-armour ambush. Orders for the ambush are set for 2130, when the NBC state is brought to 'Medium' –

Above: A special treat from the Dering Lines – a cooked breakfast. After the exhausting defensive exercise and even more testing NBC phase, hot food is extremely welcome.

Left: At the end of your withdrawal, you have to decontaminate yourselves and your equipment. Knowing you will soon be free of respirator, you perform the drills with a hearty sense of relief.

providing a clue to the next phase of the exercise.

The ambush parties set out in the early hours of Tuesday morning, and the ambushes are sprung at 0400. After withdrawing to the platoon defensive position, you barely have time to settle in before an enemy armoured vehicle trundles along the road below your hill. A short, sharp fire-fight ensues, during which you are forced to abandon your trenches and hurry uphill to where a muddy path will lead you out through the forest to eventual safety.

Losing your identity

As you wait on the track for the rest of the platoon to struggle up the steep incline, the platoon commander tells you that he has just received a radio message:

"A chemical attack is imminent, so put on your respirators now, to save

struggling to put them on later. . ."

You pull on the unpopular respirator and then move out, lugging weapons including a GPMG SF kit and 84-mm Carl Gustav as well as your weighty Bergens. Despite the slow pace, it is heavy going. It is virtually impossible to take in enough air through the respirator's filter, so that you are permanently fighting for breath. What's more, both eyepieces have a tendency to mist over, which seriously restricts your vision. It's a wholly unpleasant, claustrophobic experience.

To make matters worse, the route out is extremely wet and slippery. You keep sliding off the track, tumbling into muddy puddles. You curse and swear and struggle on, feeling quite alone despite the fact that everyone else is in the same predicament. An NBC suit with its respirator makes you acutely aware that you really are only a small part of a vast machine.

Having lost his individual identity, everyone becomes just another nondescript figure in a black, rubber mask.

Ready for breakfast

Eventually, and with considerable relief, you reach your destination – a decontamination point consisting of three taped-off enclosures. You line up and pass through each, several bodies at a time. In the first enclosure are tubs of bleach slurry solution and buckets of water. You use a brush to apply the solution which, in reality, would be left on for 15 minutes before being rinsed off with the water. In the second enclosure, you decontaminate with Fuller's Earth, using a DKP pad

After a long, chilly afternoon waiting you can at last hurry into the Chinook which will take you on to the final exercise. Called 'Flying Picquet', it is a live firing company attack.

Fighting Fit

for the job, or sprinkling yourself liberally with 'puffer' bottles. After entering the final enclosure, your mate helps cut away your old NBC suit and you replace it with a new one.

With the NBC phase at an end, you join the other three platoons in emptying magazines and pouches of blank ammunition in preparation for Flying Picquet, a live-firing exercise involving everyone on the course.

After a welcome hot breakfast, brought out from Dering Lines, you disperse into a nearby harbour area to wait for the platoon commander's orders. At 1000, you are briefed on the forthcoming company attack – to take place in and around a long valley. You will be flown to the start line by Chinook, one platoon at a time. Each platoon will furnish a reserve section, with the other sections leap-frogging forward in a series of attacks against various objectives.

Cold comfort

By 1300 you are waiting at the edge of a forest for the first lift, scheduled for 1330. By 1345, the Chinook still hasn't materialised, and the weather is now getting decidedly chilly. At 1400, you detect the unmistakable whump-whump-whump of the massive helicopter's rotors. Seconds later, the Chinook bobs up over a rise to your left, flying *very* slow and *very* low before settling on to the LZ, where it promptly shuts down!

Now what? As if in answer, the heavens open, and a bitterly cold wind gets up. You huddle in the miserable weather for nearly two more hours, and don't get aboard the helicopter until 1545. Minutes later, you land at the training area and move straight into the attack.

The weather has now deteriorated to the extent where first one man, followed by another, then another, go down with hypothermia and have to be medevaced off the area. Conditions are atrocious, with an icy rain blowing off the hills into the valley through which you must advance.

Happy ending

Despite all this, the attack goes well. Many of those who lead were, until very recently, used to obeying commands rather than giving them. Yet each objective is dealt with in a thoroughly professional manner, with the minimum of fuss. At about 2015 your section is delegated to destroy two bunkers as the final task of the exercise. The staff have unanimously agreed to cancel an attack scheduled for that night. They are quite satisfied

A 'casualty' is carried out by stretcher at the height of the action. The appalling weather and terrain make this very hard work: a stark reminder of how difficult this would be in wartime.

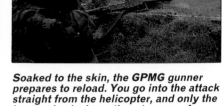

Soaked to the skin, the GPMG gunner prepares to reload. You go into the attack straight from the helicopter, and only the heavy physical exertion stops you from freezing up in the bitter cold.

with your efforts and feel that little would be gained by carrying on in weather like this.

At 2030 comes the long-awaited command:

"Stop! Apply your safety catches. Stand up, and close in to me!"

Endex! With Flying Picquet over, there are only two days of end-of-course admin to go. Of the 131 candidates who arrived at Brecon six weeks previously, 124 are left, of whom 122 will return to their units knowing they have successfully completed the Section Commanders Battle Course.

It is no mean achievement. As the Sergeant Major, JNCOs Division is apt to say: "Anybody who passes the course is a bloody good NCO!"

Kicking up a shower of earth and stones, an HE grenade takes care of an enemy bunker. It is at moments like this when you are very tired and there's a lot happening that mistakes can happen. Hence the value of drills that are second nature.

The height of the battle during the afternoon. The weather soon deteriorates even further and the scheduled night attack is cancelled. Endex is finally called at 2030 hrs and the course is over.

Everyone is completely drained, and most of you crash out in the lorry on the way back to Dering Lines. Only the next day does it really sink in that you've made it. You have passed!